The
Pilot
Maker

THE PILOT MAKER

By Lloyd L. Kelly
as told to Robert B. Parke

■

FOREWORD BY
ALAN B. SHEPARD, JR.

GROSSET & DUNLAP
A NATIONAL GENERAL COMPANY
Publishers • New York

This book is dedicated to all those wonderful individuals who have helped the evolution of the early Pilot Maker to today's sophisticated simulator and its broad contribution to man's safety. We would like to recognize especially the contribution of the Link Foundation to the development and education of those students who will become leaders in its further growth in the future.

FOREWORD

The Link Trainer has full justification to be called "The Pilot-Maker" and the first flight simulator. Thanks to his invention in the late 1920's, Ed Link was able to develop safe and inexpensive methods of teaching man to use one of the relatively new techniques of the day, flying by instruments. The original Link Trainer was a relatively simple device compared to modern simulators. However, it *was* a *moving* base trainer and could simulate the roll, pitch, or yaw of a real airplane.

The Link Trainer was not a simulator in today's sense of the word. It did not resemble a particular aircraft or provide all mission phases experienced by a pilot; but it was a valuable step toward the more complex equipment which the engineers and astronauts use today in preparing for the space missions of tomorrow.

In this book, Lloyd Kelly takes the reader through the development of the original Link Pilot-Maker to the modern aircraft and space simulators. In addition to training, today's simulators can be designed as research and engineering tools. Entire weapons systems for military uses and transportation systems for commercial use can be simulated.

Owing to the capability to evaluate mission and specific

flight problems by simulation, control and propulsion systems can be tailored to the airframe without the disastrous possibilities resulting from flight test trial-and-error. It was a necessary outgrowth of the increasingly complex and expensive aircraft that were being turned out. The test pilot's knowledge of the vehicle he would eventually fly also began to increase. He flew the engineering simulations and evaluated the various control system parameters, cockpit displays, and propulsion system characteristics. His findings had a definite influence on the direction in which the development program progressed. He actually grew up with the aircraft.

In the manned spaceflight program, we thoroughly research each mission before we fly it since many of the conditions of spaceflight will be encountered by us for the first time, such as landing on the moon.

Since the complexity and cost of each space mission prohibits training flights, the simulator assumes greater importance in the preparation of the pilot and procedures for the mission. The astronaut can review the mission plan on a daily basis, preparing for problems which he might encounter even though perhaps only once in a thousand times. But since he must react quickly to any given set of circumstances, the hours he logs for simulated emergencies are perhaps most valuable of all.

One long-range concept includes the idea of carrying along certain simulators on long space flights. During a several-month interplanetary voyage, crew members could lose some of the skill they have developed in such maneuvers as earth atmospheric reentry. It should not be difficult to plug a simple simulation device into the onboard computer required for spacecraft guidance and control. Setting up a simulator will then largely involve inserting a new program into the computer.

But the primary functions of simulators will be retained. First, the pilot must be thoroughly familiar with the correct operation of his vehicle so he will be able to detect any failure which could occur and perform under any emergency situation. Second, the simulator acts as a research tool to save time and money.

The reader of this book not only will see how Link Trainers contributed to the development of the aviation industry, but how simulators are helping develop a safer and more carefully planned program for accomplishing our future goals in air and in space. Congratulations to Lloyd Kelly and Robert Parke for a job well done.

ALAN B. SHEPARD, JR.

CONTENTS

The
Pilot
Maker

1

Flying on the Ground

On July 20, 1969, man first landed on the moon. But Astronauts Neil Armstrong and Edwin "Buzz" Aldrin had been through the maneuvers necessary for this landing of their space craft thousands of times—thanks to the Lunar Module Mission Simulator. If you recall that historic flight, you will remember Armstrong's famous words as he came in for the landing: "Everything is going A-OK. It throttles down . . . better than the simulator."

True, the simulator employed in the training of the Astronauts for their moon landing—like most of the equipment used in the Lunar Missions—was the most sophisticated ever built. But, it must be remembered that simulation is not a newcomer to aviation and space flight. As a matter of fact, aviation and simulation have been bedfellows since man's very first attempts to fly.

Man's first desire to fly was undoubtedly inspired through envious observations of the birds, and his first attempts at flight were nothing more than imitations—or *simulation*. Webster's says that a simulator is "a laboratory device that enables the operator to reproduce under test conditions phenomena likely to occur in actual performance."

Today, of course, simulators in aviation are used for

many different purposes. Some are used in laboratories and test areas to help design aircraft and space vehicles, others to help train and condition the flight crews who operate both civil and military aircraft as well as space vehicles.

But the employment of simulators is *not* limited to airborne vehicles. There are simulators to train deck officers on our merchant ships, employees of atomic electric plants, engineers on our railroads and young automobile drivers. Building simulators has become a highly competitive, multi-million-dollar industry that occupies the time of thousands of skilled persons. Even so, the name that was first and is still the leader in simulation is LINK.

This is understandable, since the man who is generally credited with planting the seed that grew into today's vast simulator industry is named Edwin Albert Link. In the years since he built his first "pilot-maker" in 1929, the company he founded has supplied trainers by the thousands to civil aviation, to the armed services, to the space program, to schools and to various transportation industries.

It was the idea of saving money that really prompted Ed Link to invent the first operational trainer. He was one of that breed of early aviator who learned to fly in the days when aviation training was as expensive as it was casual. Young Link spent most of his spare time, and what money he could afford, in and on an airplane. Eventually, he became a qualified flight instructor, but he remained concerned about the high cost of training which he felt was keeping many flying enthusiasts away from airplanes. Flight time cost twenty-five to fifty dollars an hour in many places back in the 1920's.

Besides being expensive, the airplane was, in Ed Link's

2

view, a terrible place to learn to fly. It was noisy, bumpy, uncomfortable, unstable and generally frightening to a student. The wonder, says Ed Link, was that anyone learned the delicate art of piloting an airplane in this hostile and anxiety-producing environment. It was Ed's belief that the best place to learn the rudiments of flying was in a training device, firmly rooted to the ground and situated in a warm and friendly classroom atmosphere. In such a trainer students could become familiar with the controls, responses and instruments of an airplane before leaving the hangar.

Just as attempts to sustain controlled flight were underway long before the Wright brothers did so in 1903, attempts to simulate flight were made before Link successfully did so with his trainer. Two of the first attempts were billed as "The Sanders' Teacher" and "The Eardly-Billing Oscillator." Here in the words of the December 10, 1910, issue of FLIGHT INTERNATIONAL is a description, in part, of "The Sanders' Teacher":

> Those wishing to take up aviation either as a recreation or a profession find many drawbacks at the commencement of their undertaking, but one of the most formidable, especially to those not blessed with a long purse, is the risk of smashing the machine while endeavoring to learn how to control and fly it.
>
> Even the most apt pupil is certain to find himself in difficulties at some time or another during his probation, and owing to lack of skill the machine is necessarily sacrificed to save his life, or at least to prevent a serious accident. The invention, therefore, of a device which will enable the novice to obtain a clear conception of the workings of the control of an aeroplane, and of the conditions existent in the air, without any risk personally or otherwise, is to be welcomed without a doubt. Several have al-

ready been constructed to this end, and the Sanders' Teacher is the latest to enter the field.

The aim and object of an invention of this kind is naturally to render tuition safe to the pupil while at the same time giving him confidence. Now there is a tendency to design such an apparatus merely for purposes of balance and without any real resemblance to an actual aeroplane, while the very balance is so exaggerated that the pupil is placed under conditions that are in no way so arduous in free flight.

. . . All these details are standard parts of the Sanders' biplane and can be substituted if desired by the same parts of any other type of aeroplane. Thus, the purchaser of a Teacher is buying parts which can be used later if he wishes in the construction of a machine and his outlay can therefore scarcely be considered an extravagant one.

Unfortunately, the Teacher was not successful, and it was another nineteen years before Link had his trainer operating successfully.

My introduction to the Link Trainer took place long before I met the man who invented it. My first encounter with the "blue box," as it was called, was in basic flight training in Greenville, Mississippi, in 1942. As I recall, we had only four of these devices, and each student was scheduled in the Link for instrument training before he had *any* instruction in the air. I had been through several sessions in the Link and was doing well enough, but I couldn't fly formation in the BT13 trainer airplane to save my soul. In despair, my instructor put me up for elimination check flight. The day of my "washout" flight dawned and it turned out to be a gloomy one. There was a 400-foot ceiling, and as I climbed into the

4

white-nosed single-engine trainer, I noticed lots of holes in the panel. I looked at the Form 1A which showed the airplane's status. It said "gyro instruments out." Well, I scarcely knew what a gyro was and didn't feel competent to fly on instruments anyway.

Another student and I were supposed to fly in formation on either side of the instructor's ship. We took off and promptly entered the clouds. The instructor radioed us to "tuck in close," and shortly we broke out on top. We flew formation more or less together and finally the instructor asked me to take the lead. I went up front, and as we approached some clouds, I started to turn away. The instructor, however, radioed to go right through.

Knowing that I was expected to fly on instruments, I stared at the panel. It was then I first realized that a turn needle was a gyro instrument, and where this all-important instrument should have been was a great big hole. I tried to use the magnetic compass and airspeed indicator, but when we broke out of the cloud, the formation was in a diving turn. The instructor called me and told me to get back on his wing and we started back in the clouds.

Now I fully realized my predicament and frantically called to him, saying, "Sir, I don't have any instruments." I thought he shook his head in disbelief, and then we plunged back into the clouds. I flew as close a formation as I knew how, when suddenly he signalled a breakup. He disappeared down through the clouds, followed by the other student. And there I was 3000 feet up in a BT13 with not much more than holes for instruments. I didn't know enough to be frightened, though I knew I would have to let down alone without instruments. I had been taught the proper let-down speed was 120 miles per hour and 500 feet per minute, so down I went.

Of course, I couldn't hold a heading since there was only the compass as a directional instrument, but I got 120 and came back on the throttle and fought the plane down. Miraculously, I came out of the clouds about 600 feet, going more or less straight. I wasn't sure just where I was, but soon found a familiar bridge and found my way back to the base. I landed and arrived just as the squadron leader was telling the other student that he was washed out.

I walked up to him and he said, "Kelly, you didn't do too badly on formation, but when you led the flight, you went in a spiral! You can't fly instruments. I had better recommend you for elimination." Aghast, I said, "But, sir, didn't you hear my call?" He said he hadn't and asked me about it. When I told him I had no instruments and that I thought he understood this, he blanched and put in a call to maintenance. They confirmed the fact that my plane had no gyro instruments. His parting shot to me was, "Kelly, anybody with your Irish luck is bound to get through." He let me stay.

I went on and successfully completed my training, but the experience made a lasting impression on me. It was clear that if the airplane was to become a reliable means of transportation or a major military vehicle, it would have to have all-weather capability. That meant that pilots would have to be able to fly as precisely on instruments as they did in clear weather. Though there were still a great many flyers in the Air Force and out of it who believed any good pilot could handle "blind flying" by the seat of his pants, I was confident that instrument flying was a new science and that Link training was going to be a major factor in the evolution of that science.

During the remainder of my training I tried to perfect my instrument flying skills, and after winning my wings, I was assigned to flight instruction duty. I passed on my conviction that instrument flying was flight of the future, and endlessly encouraged my students to make the most of their Link instruction.

Although the early Link Trainers were far from perfect, they did offer a student the opportunity to review procedures and to experience in a ground-based trainer what the instruments could tell him about his "blind flying" techniques. The older model Link Trainers leaned and lurched and wheezed as the students manipulated the controls. It was not much like flying an airplane, but there was movement and it was generally consistent with what an airplane could be expected to do if the controls were moved similarly. It was clear, however, that with the increasing dependence of both the military and the commercial carriers on instrument flying, more sophisticated trainers would have to be developed. My intense interest in this subject finally brought me in touch with the inventor of the Link Trainer.

It was while stationed at Bryan Air Base in Texas that I first met Ed Link. While these were only brief encounters, one day I was sent to the main plant of Link Aviation, Inc., in Binghamton in upstate New York. The purpose of the trip was to evaluate a new trainer. It was on this junket that I got to know and admire Ed Link and decided that I'd like to work for Link after my military service. I hoped this would be an opportunity to combine my pre-war teaching with my military flying experience.

7

Fortunately for me, Philip S. Hopkins, a vice president and corporate lawyer for Link Aviation, as well as president of the Board of Education in Binghamton, believed that aviation was going to become such an important part of our culture that it should be taught in the public schools. Learning of this from Ed during my Binghamton visit, I wrote Phil a letter on my return to Bryan Air Base, and told him I'd be leaving the service soon and would like to work at Link.

I received a telegram back saying they would like to have me at $300 per month—three times what I had made as a teacher, and half of what I was making as a captain. I had also been offered a job with the Civil Aeronautics Administration at Fort Worth, Texas, as a flight inspector at $400 per month. In 1945, both salaries were quite satisfactory, but the opportunity seemed better at Link, so off I flew to Binghamton.

During my first day at work, Ed Link invited me to his office so he could learn more about me. On my arrival the glass-paneled door opened and Ed asked me to come in. Being fresh from the service, I stood rigid at attention, almost ready to give him a salute. Ed said, "What are you doing that for, Lloyd? Come on in and sit down." He asked me to tell him about myself.

About that time the door of his office came open with a bang and in walked Tony, one of the maintenance men, who said, "Where's the key to the store room, Ed?" Again my military background responded—a private coming in that way to a general's office—and I waited for the fireworks to begin. Ed's reaction was, "Gee, Tony, I'm sorry. I should have left that open." He then gave Tony the key and Tony

8

went out to do his job. This was my first lesson in the Link environment, and one I'll remember about the inventor of the trainer and the firm he founded—everyone's job performance contributes to the success of a company.

Flight simulators have changed greatly in the years that I have been associated with Link. Today, they are extremely complex electronic devices which are employed on the ground to provide crews a realistic environment for practicing in-flight techniques and procedures. They are used in virtually all phases of training, both for preparing fledgling pilots for their first flights, and for helping experienced flight crews maintain and increase their proficiency or make a smooth transition to a new type aircraft.

Basically, a typical modern flight simulator consists of three major elements: a detailed replica of the cockpit or flight deck of a given aircraft; an instructor's console equipped with duplicate cockpit instruments, graphic flight recorders and various controls; and a computer section which electronically translates pilot actions into instrument indications and cockpit motion. But to fully appreciate the value and effectiveness of today's electronic simulators, one must first have a basic understanding of the conditions under which high speed jet flight is conducted.

Jet flight is no longer an art—it's a science. The hotshot pilot who flew by the "seat of his pants," and who relied on an occasional glance out his window to determine his location and heading, has been replaced by a precisely trained, cool-headed technician, who must rely almost exclusively on his instruments, radar and radio equipment from takeoff to touchdown. But, in order to rely on his equipment, he must first know how to use it. This requires extensive training.

That's where the simulator comes into the picture, for it is admirably equipped to duplicate with precise realism virtually all conditions of flight. In addition to control and instrument simulation, many of today's simulators are also equipped to produce cockpit motion and a visual presentation of runways and surrounding airport terrain for practice take-offs and landings.

Basically, the instrument simulation is accomplished in the following way: The pilot, seated in the simulator cockpit, is confronted with all of the controls, instruments and radio equipment that he would find in the actual aircraft, and in the same location as in the aircraft. After completing his preflight check, he "takes off," "flies" his planned course or mission, and then "lands" his simulator at the end of the problem.

As he "flies" his mission, all of his instruments react to the handling of his controls, just as they would in the actual aircraft. They tell him how high he is, how fast he is going, whether he is climbing or diving, in what direction he is headed and his geographical position. They also tell him about the condition and operation of his engine and his electrical and hydraulic systems. Further, they inform him about important weather and barometric conditions.

The instructor, during the conduct of a training problem, can introduce a variety of emergency conditions and malfunctions, and by observing his duplicate cockpit instruments and signal lights, can readily ascertain the pilot's proficiency in handling these conditions.

During a simulated flight, the instructor locates and describes the ground radio signals used as navigation aids, and also serves as controller during Ground Controlled Approach landings.

Graphic automatic flight recorders, which plot the simulated aircraft's progress on a map of the earth, are provided in the instructor's area. Recorders are provided for evaluating pilot proficiency during critical approach and landing operations.

The instrument realism provided by the simulator results from the computers, which are actuated by either the pilot's or instructor's use of the controls. These computers solve the necessary equations of flight, and in turn cause the appropriate instruments to react to simulated conditions just as they would in actual flight. In the safety of a simulator, almost any situation can be presented for a pilot-trainee's reaction to emergency conditions. The loss of one, two, three or even four engines can be simulated. The turbulence of a violent storm can be introduced, or indications of an inflight fire can be presented. Just about any conceivable emergency can be programmed.

Most of such emergency conditions should not be practiced by pilots in their airplane. The first time is the real time. But the reaction of trainees to major emergencies can be evaluated in a simulator. That is one of its great values. As strange as it may seem, so realistic are the flight characteristics of simulators that veteran pilots have been known to break into a cold sweat when they have been loaded up with simulated emergencies.

Some of today's electronic training devices have progressed far beyond the point of being "flight" simulators and can be described more accurately as mission simulators. In the space program, they have not only been used to aid in the final design of the vehicle, but also to solve much more pressing problems. During the week of April 13, 1970, the world witnessed one of the most dramatic rescues in the history of mankind. The whole world held its breath as Mission Control in Houston struggled to bring back safely to earth the crew of Apollo 13.

It's doubtful that anyone could have foreseen the crucial role simulators were to play in helping to effect the rescue of Apollo 13 after its near-disastrous explosion. Literally hundreds of potential malfunctions had been anticipated and "flown" by the astronauts in two Apollo simulators—one located at the Houston Manned Spacecraft Center and the other at the Kennedy Space Center. Procedures had been developed for each of these problems, but an explosion such as the one that racked Apollo 13 during its moon flight could not have been considered. When Commander Lovell's chilling words, "Hey, we've got a problem," came over the air, everyone connected with the space program came mentally bolt upright to see what he could do to lend a hand.

Of course the first priority was to determine the extent of the damage and to evaluate the chances of a safe return to earth. As soon as this had been done, the simulators and their instructors began to come into play as the conditions in Apollo were duplicated in the simulator. Then followed twenty-four hours of frantic work by instructors, astronauts, technicians and scientists as a plan for safe recovery was worked out in the simulators and then passed on to the threatened spacemen. During that time each set of simulators was operated for more than forty hours and the instructors and standby astronauts worked themselves to the point of exhaustion in an effort to verify by using the simulators every move the astronauts should make.

One of the first decisions that had to be made was whether or not the service module with its damaged number two cyrogenic tank could be jettisoned from the command module. This would have lightened the load to be carried by the crippled spacecraft by some 60,000 pounds, but no one knew if the remaining vehicle could be flown and controlled if this was done. The vast array of computers connected with the Apollo simulator were soon facing this problem and racing to find an answer. As standby astronauts flew the simulator in this condition, it became apparent that the craft could be handled in this configuration. As it turned out, it was not necessary to separate the service module as other solutions became apparent.

With many of the life support systems in the command module damaged or ineffective, it was quickly apparent that a retreat to the lunar module and its reserve supplies of oxygen and power was called for and the simulators were used to determine how best to handle the complex moves to be made from this position. With much of the command module (CM) electronics shut down, a critical condition of temperature in the CM had to be faced. Thermal studies had to be conducted to determine how cold the Apollo might become and whether or not a number of the subsystems might be affected by the subzero cold.

But perhaps the most critical use to which the simulators were put was in determining cockpit procedures to be followed and checklists to be used in each of the maneuvers that would be necessary if Apollo 13 were to be brought back safely. More than a dozen astronauts at both Kennedy and

Houston worked in the simulators to find the optimum moves to be made considering the short supply of consumables and power. As each step was worked out by the ground-bound astronauts, the checklists and procedures were relayed to their space-bound brothers. As every essential maneuver was performed in the simulator and the precise time line drawn for its implementation, the astronaut who had done the simulation would stand by for explanation and encouragement to the Apollo crew.

As the first important steps were successfully made and the Apollo swung around the moon and headed for home, the most crucial point in the recovery lay ahead. Reentry into earth's atmosphere still presented the most difficult problems and as all hands weathered the first days safely, all eyes turned to the impending instant when the stricken ship must hurtle into the cruel and inexorable heat of earth's atmosphere. Two days before reentry, a special controller astronaut and simulator instruction crew started work on this phase. The problems to be faced were staggering. Both the lunar module and the service module had to be separated from the command module at precisely the correct instant and the CM had to be poised in the correct trajectory before releasing its burdens. If the course to earth was not exactly right, the Apollo could skip out of the atmosphere and be lost, or plunge too steeply into the sandpaper-like blanket of air around the earth and become a flaming torch.

The special task force set to work with computers and diagrams and simulators. In addition to determining the separation timing of the lunar and service modules, there remained the task of reviving the sleeping command module to its last job of carrying its human cargo home safely. Since most of the CM system had been shut down to conserve what power remained for return, detailed studies were conducted to find the optimum sequence for bringing systems back on line. Dozens of switches and scores of circuit breakers had to be properly configured in just the right sequence. Material and equipment had to be stowed and checklists worked out for each phase of this important operation. Consultations with manufacturers of equipment were made to determine the actual and outer limits of their gear. When everything was in order, the information was passed to the tense crew members of Apollo for what turned out to be a six-and-a-half-hour reentry procedure. As the time for the payoff approached, everything was rechecked in the simulators. Consumables such as oxygen, cooling water and electrical power were watched with the greatest care as the simulator astronauts went through their dry runs. When all was ready, there was a short period of tense waiting and then the sequence started. It went like a routine mission with separation of the now excess modules occurring on schedule and the multitude of preentry steps taking place exactly as planned. Everyone connected with the rescue breathed easier when a rugged Apollo and its heroic crew hit the water on target. But to us in the simulation industry, our "baby" had functioned the way we had always expected it to.

2

The Birth of the First Simulator—The "Pilot Maker"

While Binghamton, New York, claims that it's the birthplace of the simulator, its inventor claims Huntington, Indiana, as his.

Born July 26, 1904, Ed Link was a boy of six when his family moved to Binghamton. His father, Edwin A. Link, Sr., had sold his interest in the famed Shaff Brothers Piano Company of Chicago and purchased the bankrupt remains of the Binghamton Automatic Music Company, a manufacturer of player pianos. Renaming the firm The Link Piano and Organ Company, the senior Link soon started producing player pianos and nickelodeons. If indeed the quality of the product was improved under the Link management, this could conceivably account for some of the marked increase in sales of the new company, but it's more likely that the strong personality and business acumen of Link himself was responsible.

After several years of hard work on the part of Link, the Link Player Piano was a fixture in every lodge hall, amusement gallery and pleasure palace in southern New York and northern Pennsylvania. Nor had the more dignified end of the business been neglected. Link pipe organs were to be seen in theaters, concert halls, mausoleums and private homes as far away as California and were regarded as highly as were the instruments of its better known competitor, Wurlitzer. Though it is reported to have caused Link some personal anguish, it is known that since the Link product was somewhat less expensive than the Wurlitzer, a good many theater owners of the day economized by buying the less well-known organ, but still introduced it to the hushed audience as the "mighty Wurlitzer."

Success had brought to Link and his family an economic and social position that was the equal of any in Binghamton. This was reflected in their large, comfortable stucco house and their membership in the Binghamton Country Club, where the senior Link excelled on the golf course as well as at the billiard table.

Before her marriage, Mrs. Edwin Link, Sr., had been the former Katherine Martin of Tuscola, Illinois. She was a short stocky woman with a rather stern and proper outlook. An accomplished singer and passable pianist, she had a brief fling before her marriage at performing professionally at church and social gatherings. After moving to Binghamton she was featured soloist in the First Presbyterian Church, which the family attended regularly, more at the insistence of the mother than the pere. It was she whom young Edwin resembled most in both temperament and in features, though he had his father's height.

In 1918 Ed's parents separated and Ed went with his mother back to her family's home in Chicago. Mrs. Link decided to again pursue her singing career. Rather than have Ed grow up in a big city, she sent him to live with her sister in Rockford, Illinois.

In this pleasant midwest community, with its economy divided between agriculture and a burgeoning industrial complex, Ed began in a frighteningly methodical way to start his career. After graduating from elementary school, and at the advice of his eighth-grade teacher, he entered the local vocational high school and took courses in mechanical drawing, foundry work, machine shop and elementary carpentry. With the zeal of the damned, he proceeded to steep himself in the world of the artisan, in spite of opposition from his father.

While in the '20's, vocational training didn't have the odious connotations that many "educators" place upon it today, Ed's father wanted him to go to college, just as Edwin's older brother, George, had done. Seven years older, George had gone through Hamilton College, earned his degree majoring in mathematics, and had no trouble making Phi Beta Kappa, as well as cutting quite a swath among the ladies at the same time. Link senior, being something of a gay blade himself, was much more in sympathy with the kind of youthful peccadillos attributed to George than to the apparent backwardness or disinterest in "formal" schooling exhibited by young Ed. But Mrs. Link accepted her youngest son's desires and his teacher's recommendation, and Ed was permitted to continue at Rockford Training High School.

In 1920, Ed's mother decided to move to Los Angeles. There Ed enrolled in the Los Angeles Polytechnic High School. His energy in science and mathematics seemed inexhaustible, and his curiosity about machines was limitless. In this environment, he decided it was time to learn to fly. He was able to afford his first lesson by saving spending money sent by his father and by working in a motorcycle service garage. In Ed's words:

"The first flight I ever made was with Sidney Chaplin, brother of Charlie, the famous entertainer of silent movie days. It was from a little field on Wilshire Boulevard, right where the Ambassador Hotel now stands. The airport stretched for about a half-mile in an east-west direction, and its surface was matted with ragged brown grass. As I remember it, clustered around the single modest barn-like building which served as hangar headquarters, was a nondescript array of elderly biplanes. Nearby a sign proclaimed: *Chaplin Field—Fly With the Stars—Airplane Rides—Sales and Services—Curtiss Aeroplane and Motor Company— Sidney Chaplin, Operator.*

"When I got out there to Chaplin Field on a borrowed motorcycle, Chaplin quickly introduced himself to me as my instructor. He was all duded up in riding pants and boots, leather flight jacket, a silk scarf, and helmet and goggles. I remember it was a rather hot day, but that's what aviators wore in those days. I was sure impressed.

"After giving him the fifty dollars for my one-hour lesson, I climbed up in the back seat of his Curtiss Oriole and belted myself in.

"Once Chaplin climbed in the front seat, he signalled a mechanic to prop the airplane. The mechanic braced his feet and clapped both hands on the broad propeller blade, and called 'contact.' 'Contact,' replied Chaplin, switching on the ignition. The mechanic spun the prop through and the engine caught. We taxied down the dusty runway and off we went.

"For the better part of that hour we did loops and spins and buzzed everything in sight. Thank heaven I didn't get sick, but when we got down, I hadn't touched the controls at all. I thought, 'That's a hell of a way to teach someone to fly.' But I made a date for the next week anyway.

"I had two more lessons with Sidney, and they were pretty much like the first one. He did let me put my hands and feet on the controls during the maneuvers so that I could feel what he was doing. I didn't learn too much, however. I found out later that most of the old-time aviators, like Chaplin, started teaching their students by scaring them half to death."

The next fall, at Ed's father's insistence, he was sent to Bellefonte Academy, Bellefonte, Pennsylvania. This fine preparatory school, in Link senior's opinion, would be the institution most likely to succeed in developing his son's hidden scholastic talents. But after four months Ed left the Academy and rejoined his mother in Chicago. Latin, History and Elementary French didn't make an impression on him as the vocational subjects had. On his return to the midwest city, he went to work for Western Electric Company.

While employed there, his mechanical ability was quickly spotted by his foreman. On his recommendation, Ed was transferred to the company's mechinist apprentice program. Again, however, the family stepped in. This time his brother, George, suggested that Ed come live with him in Wheeling, West Virginia, and attend Lindsley Institute, a fine military school that represented itself as specializing in behavioral problems of young men. While Ed wasn't a behavioral problem, he *was* an academic one. He liked the military life, but he couldn't tolerate the dreary classwork.

Thus, when his brother's insurance firm transferred him to Kansas City, Missouri, later in the school year, Ed rejoined his mother, who had returned to Binghamton.

In 1922 young Ed entered Binghamton Central High School, but once again he fled the academic life, and this finished his formal schooling.

Once he left school completely, Ed went to work for the Link Piano and Organ Company. He proudly recalls, "When I went to work in my father's factory, I started right at the bottom learning how to build pianos and tuning the organs. It sure wasn't what I had in mind for a career, but it's curious how if a man puts his mind to what comes to hand, it often works out for the best. I'm certain that if I hadn't had that experience, I never would have been able to build the first pilot-maker."

Ed's spare time was spent in taking apart and reassembling a motorcycle. He made extra money haunting the local garages and offering his assistance in repairing almost any machine that needed attention. When unable to stir up any action in this field, he could be found in his room listening to the faint and fuzzy signals from radio station KDKA in Pittsburgh on his crystal set. So novel was radio in those days that Ed was called on by the local theater manager to give a display of the wonders of the crystal set on the stage. His curiosity and interest in the radio even brought him to view the inside of the local library for the first time as he looked for books that could explain the principles of the wireless. Unfortunately, there was less guidance in this subject in the library than there was in the advertising columns of *Popular Science,* a source to which he often resorted.

Though wireless and motorcycles and the products of The

Link Piano and Organ Company took most of his time, he still dreamed of becoming a pilot. As he tells it, his earliest memories of flying were picked up from newspaper accounts of the aviation news of World War I. When the heroes came back in 1919 and 1920 with their Jenny airplanes and began to give air shows all over the country during what was to become known later as the "barnstorming days," Ed yearned to be one of them. His family, with typical upstate conservatism, discouraged his interest in airplanes and recited the canards about the people who were identified with them. It was universally accepted that all pilots were irresponsible bums and were little better than gypsies.

To be sure many of the pilots of the early twenties were known to be an unruly, irresponsible, hard-drinking lot. They made their living roaming the country in their broken-down airplanes, performing at airshows or taking passengers for brief rides at anywhere from one to five dollars each. They made a lot of money when the weather and the curiosity of the community they were visiting was high, and they made little or nothing otherwise. In either case, they were reputed to return to the local economy whatever they made through the good offices of the neighborhood speakeasy. True there was a cadre of serious-minded people in aviation, but they were to be found largely in the military or in one of the several aircraft manufacturing companies then starting in business.

To many people of that day the barnstormers were like a plague of locusts. During the summer months hundreds of two- and three-man groups would go barnstorming around the country. Air shows hadn't grown to the point of being the aerial circuses that were prevalent during the late 1920's and early '30's.

Generally, barnstorming consisted of three or four pilots getting together with their airplanes and dropping in on a small town. It was customary to announce themselves as war heroes. Although many of these fliers had been in the war, few had flown in combat. Many of them had simply been in training in the United States, or acted as instructors, and in many cases had simply been taught to fly by someone who had been in combat.

While Ed had taken his first lessons in 1920, it was six years later before he had another one. In the spring of '26, he took several lessons from Richard "Dick" Bennett, who operated Bennett Field in Binghamton. While installing an organ on Long Island, he also had several more hours of training at Curtiss Field. In addition, he travelled on the weekends with the local barnstormers. Even though they didn't let him fly their airplanes, Ed would go along as the ticket taker, the mechanic, helper, or the guy who would polish the windshields. This is what one had to do to learn the barnstorming business and to get to know the people with whom one aspired to fly. After six or eight months apprenticeship, a few flights would be allowed and gradually a new pilot would be born. Ed picked up a few hours this way until Alfred Stanley, World War I Ace, from whom he was taking lessons, finally let him solo. Ed considers this the *first* accomplishment of his life.

While his mother, even in her rather cold stern fashion, was rather proud of Ed, his father was furious when he learned of his son's involvement in aviation. He promptly fired Ed. For over a month, Link senior tried to extract from Mrs. Link and from Ed a promise that Ed would give up aviation. Ed refused. Having been connected with Ed for over twenty-five years, I know that he can be a very stubborn guy when he thinks he's right.

During his period of forced unemployment at the organ factory, Ed's interest and involvement in aviation deepened and he even earned a little money from the flying business. The barnstormers that he traveled with began to pay him (only a couple of dollars a week) for the odd jobs he performed for them. This small stipend, together with some spending money from his mother kept him going and at last his father had to give in and take him back at the factory.

Actually, George Thayer, general manager and superintendent of the factory, put a great deal of pressure on the elder Link and had even gone so far as to threaten to quit his post with the company. His absence had seemed to emphasize to his father and Thayer the fact that Ed had become one of the few people skilled in the art of building and tuning organs. He excelled, too, at repairing player pianos and was considered to be an expert at reviving the most battered and decrepit instruments to working order. It was these unique skills and a sense of the inevitable that forced Ed's father to yield to his son's determination to continue with an interest in aviation.

In 1924, young Link obtained the first of his many patents. This was for a suction device to pick lint off the piano roll. "It was a simple little thing," Ed told me, "designed to make my job easier. Most of the service calls on the piano were made because dust or dirt would clog the air holes in the player-piano roll, and the thing would stop altogether or sound so awful that nobody could stand it. So I rigged a tiny vacuum cleaner to the bellows and as the roll passed in front of it, all the dust would be sucked into a container. It worked fine and made me a little money, too."

Ed did a great deal of traveling for the Link Company in those days and often headed the organ installation crews. On one such trip to install an organ at Jenson's Melrose Theater, Los Angeles, he had to contend with the unexpected. On this job six weeks had been spent in erecting the Link organ in the theater, and final tuning was performed the day before the dedication was to take place. Ed and his crew were standing by for the big day. They had returned to their hotel for a little rest when California was shaken by an earthquake. The Link crew rushed to the theater to discover that huge chunks of ceiling plaster had crashed into the organ chambers and had all but filled the open resonators. The great and near-great of the movie world were to be on hand for the opening, and the reputation of the Link organ was at stake. Ed led his crew in a burst of feverish activity during the next day, and the job was finished as the first guests arrived.

Even though Ed was working full-time at the organ factory, he continued to devote his spare time to aviation. He took flying lessons whenever he could afford them and he followed the barnstormers on weekends. As his dedication to aviation became increasingly apparent, so too did his need to have his own airplane. As all of us who have worked with Ed Link know, he can be a most persuasive fellow. He must have been all of that when, in spite of his mother's reservations about aviation, he persuaded her to lend him money to buy his first airplane, a Cessna Model AA.

The files of the Cessna Aircraft Company of Wichita, Kansas, indicate that a Mr. E. A. Link, Binghamton, New York, was the original owner of Cessna Model AA, serial number 114. This AA was powered by a 120-horsepower Anzani engine. The Department of Commerce (forerunner of the Federal Aviation Administration—FAA) records list the AA as a "Cessna 4-120" (four-place, 120-horsepower craft). Cessna records further show that this airplane, with a DOC registration 4156, was delivered February 28, 1928. This was less than sixty days after the incorporation date of Cessna Aircraft Company and was the first airplane delivered by this now world-famous aircraft manufacturer.

With his own airplane, Ed was finally in a position to cash in on the investment of time and money he had spent in aviation. Weekends and evenings were spent with his airplane as he tried to find ways of making the airplane pay for itself. He did charter and ferry work in addition to barnstorming and air shows, and as it became clear that with luck, a living could be made from aviation, he left his full-time job at the organ factory.

At best the life of the aviator in the '20's was an insecure one. Engines were unreliable and each pilot had to be his own mechanic. At worst Ed figured he would encounter an engine failure and subsequent forced landing every ten hours. On such occasions, when the airplane ended up in a farmer's field, the barbed wire from a nearby fence would quite often be used to make repairs. However, Ed had an advantage over many of the barnstormers in that his sensitivity to sound and vibrations allowed him to detect trouble in his engine before it quit completely.

In the summer of 1928, Ed went into barnstorming in a

big way. The formula that was used was simple enough. It involved getting two or three fellow pilots (Ed's group was usually made up of himself, Gardner "Peg" Nagel, Al Stanley or Harold Bowen), each of whom had an airplane at his disposal. If the weather looked good the night before, the group would get together and decide where in the western New York or northern Pennsylvania areas they would work. In the early morning they would start out, arriving in midmorning over the target town. One of the members of the formation would break off and try to draw a crowd by doing some spins and rolls over the town. This would be accompanied by abrupt cutting of the engine and forcing it to backfire so it would appear that the pilot was in trouble. In some cases, part of the come-on included gliding down behind a hill with the engine cut so it would look like the airplane was certain to crash. At the last minute, the airplane would recover and swoop up out of the valley. As soon as everybody in town was gaping at them, one of the group would land in a nearby field and negotiate with the owners as to the conditions for using the field. The cost could range anywhere from providing free rides for the owner and his family to as much as twenty to twenty-five dollars a day in cash. If negotiations were satisfactory, a signal was given to the others to come in and land, and the day's work of taking the local citizens for a ride would begin. The prices were literally anything the traffic would bear. For openers, rides would start at five dollars. If business was slow, the price dropped to five dollars a couple. The duration of the ride varied too according to the press of business. The earlier rides would be a leisurely trip around the town, and often the pilot would show the passenger his house from the air. If business was brisk and the price went down, the ride would be a brief spin around the field, sometimes lasting less than a minute. If the weather was good and the interest of the townspeople high, flying would continue up to dusk and the happy barnstormers could pocket a couple of thousand dollars in a weekend's flying.

The barnstormers were not above picking up an occasional instructional dollar. There would always be a young person hanging around, and the young people were usually the first to arrive on the field. They would choose a likely looking fellow who seemed interested in getting near the airplane to take the tickets, get the customers lined up and help sell the folks on the idea of taking rides.

On some occasions a convert to flying emerged from these junkets and the barnstormers would thus acquire a student. The cost of lessons would be adjusted to whatever the trainee could afford, and could range between ten dollars to fifty dollars an hour. It was very much a matter of milking the situation for as much as there was in it. Of course, few pilots knew anything about teaching since instructor's licenses didn't come into being until the '30's.

I believe it was pretty close to the mid-'20's before any kind of license was involved. In 1928 there were more than 5,000 licensed pilots in the United States. In the early days you either flew without a license or later on you got a private license simply by asking for it. You didn't have to do anything but ask. Later, when Ed received his license, there was a slight change in the procedure. That is, he received a "letter of authority" from the Department of Commerce in 1927 for his limited commercial rating, which he obtained by just saying that he was ready to take the test for this license.

The letter of authority gave him all the privileges of the rating, and it was almost a year later before he actually took the test with the DOC inspector. Tradition and a sense of self-preservation dictated that the inspector told the would-be licensee what to do and then observed the maneuvers from the ground.

There were two other pilot ratings in those days: commerce and transport. Both were issued when the pilot accumulated a minimum number of air hours, but no test was given. The pilots kept the record of their flight time in log books, but they required no authorization or proof of time. In the early '30's, of course, a full test was required for all ratings, much as it is today.

The conventional method of teaching a person to fly in Ed's day was to subject the student to a kind of torture test. The aspirant would be taken aloft and subjected to every sick-making movement in the instructor's repertoire. If the student survived and wanted more, it was certain he would become a good pilot. If he walked away from the airplane in disgust, the conclusion was that he would never have been a pilot anyway.

Many of the barnstorming pilots were loathe to let anyone fly their plane solo because often this was the only possession they had. Thus, pre-solo training would drag on and on. It was not uncommon for a student to have fifteen or twenty hours before being allowed to solo. After solo, the cost remained high and it was difficult to accumulate enough flying time to become proficient.

During the later part of 1927, before he had his own airplane, Ed saw that his own skills were never going to improve unless he could get more practice than he could ever afford at that time. He remembered that on one lesson he had at Curtiss Field, the instructor would not allow him to fly, but did permit him to sit in the plane and taxi it alone. Ed found that he could gain some feel of the airplane this way, and he persuaded some of his airplane-owning friends to let him build up time this way. He discovered later that the French in World War I had used this method to train their pilots. Called the "penguin system," it allowed would-be flyers to get the feel of the craft's controls while staying on the ground.

Ed read everything he could about the penguin system since he felt that it had a great deal of merit. Although Great Britain and the United States didn't use this system, Ed found that the French pilots were considered tops during the war and their training time was a fraction of that of other systems. Ed began to wonder at that point why he couldn't build a device that would provide all movements and motions of taxiing aircraft and thus would allow preliminary flight instruction to be given on the ground. It would be a shortcut to flying, he reasoned, and could bring training costs down to a more reasonable figure. He began to construct a simulated cockpit that could be set up anywhere, yet could move and respond to controls similar to that of an airplane.

In the evenings, after work at the organ factory, Ed would taxi up and down Bennett Field in one of his friend's airplanes. He wanted his device to duplicate the responses and have the feel he experienced as he taxied the airplane. It was only natural that Ed would think of using air pressure to provide movements in his device since he had a great deal of experience with the forced air principles used in the organ and player piano. The organ used an electric motor (originally it was by a manual pump) to work a series of bellows to force air into the great pipes that produced the sounds of the organ. The piano, too, used an electric motor and bellows in series to create either suction or pressure to activate the hammers against the strings of the piano. An endless roll of paper with perforations punched in it would pass by a series of holes connected to hoses each directed to a key. As the hole would permit air through the hose, the keys would be activated.

Ed used a motor and bellows borrowed from his father's factory to provide the force to tip and turn the device as the stick and rudder were moved. Thus a student could become accustomed to a conventional stick-and-rudder bar and to what generally would happen in an airplane as the controls were moved. The whole unit sat on a universal joint and was moved by a series of bellows and motors that would gasp and wheeze as it whirled around to give the effect of an airplane in motion.

Work progressed slowly on the trainer in the basement of the organ factory. Ed found it was most difficult to duplicate the feel of a moving aircraft. It took almost a year and a half to give his trainer the proper response of a moving airplane. In the early part of 1929 it was, however, made operational after a great deal of time and expense for the gas and oil used for taxiing on the ground. Phil Hopkins filed a patent for Ed Link on April 14 of that year. Phil's cost of the patent filing to Ed was sixty dollars, plus several flying lessons. Thus, the first flight trainer had seen the light of day from the basement of The Link Piano and Organ Company and the age of simulation was under way.

3

The Army Takes the
Trainer

The first advertisement for the pilot-maker which appeared in 1929 listed the Link Aviation Trainer as "an efficient aeronautical training aid—a novel, profitable amusement feature."

As an efficient aeronautical training aid, the trainer proved itself conclusively when Ed taught his brother George to fly with only forty-two minutes of actual flight time in an airplane, after George had taken a concentrated six-hour course in the trainer. George adds a little more to the story, however. While his solo flight was successful, he broke the cabane strut on landing about eight hours later and never flew again. He had had enough of flying and jokingly remarked that he felt Ed was using him as a guinea pig anyway.

As a novel, profitable, amusement feature, several veteran amusement park operators were interested in the device. Ed went so far as to install a mechanism in his trainer that permitted it to accept coins. Thus the pilot-maker joined the coin-operated hobbyhorses that still abound in penny arcades and five-and-dime stores. A feature built in for amusement use was an efficiency indicator. A numbered dial scored a point against the operator—up to a possible fifteen—each time the trainer left the level flight attitude. The degree of skill could be determined accordingly. Many amusement park operators offered prizes for low scores.

The acceptance of the device as an aviation novelty was noted in the November 1930 issue of *Science and Invention:*

> The Link Aviation Trainer is the name of a device to teach potential aviators the art of flying. This consists of a single seater monoplane-like structure that is as sensitive as a real plane. If the operator does not properly control the stick, and have the ailerons and rudder in the correct position, all of the sensations of a side slip, nose dive, or a near loop are experienced. An electric motor supplying air to a bellows, produces the flying effect. A small light on the nose of the plane indicates to the ground pilot when the stick has not been properly controlled, while an indicator tallies every error. The device is the center of attraction at the Mayfair Miniature Golf Course in Los Angeles, California, where it was first installed. Such devices would make a valuable adjunct to the multitude of miniature golf courses that now dot the country.

With the pilot-maker scorned as a training device and relegated to the equivalent of a toy, Ed decided to start his own school and use the pilot-maker as the foundation of his training program.

With the permission of George Thayer, who was the manager of the Link plant, he used the basement of the organ factory as a ground school classroom and location for his trainer. The Link Flying School then made a fabulous announcement to all would-be-aviators: a guaranteed "learn to fly for eighty-five dollars" offer. This worked out roughly to thirty-five dollars for ground school, all given in the trainer, and two hours of flight time at twenty-five dollars per hour. The plan brought students to solo only, which, without the use of the trainer, might have taken as many as fifteen or more hours.

At first the school did very well. In 1930 over one hundred persons soloed at the school. But after the 1929 Depression set in, Ed's fortunes plummeted. Few people could afford eighty-five dollars to learn anything as impractical as flying and few could spend money on something as unnecessary as a piano or an organ. Radios and phonographs were coming into widespread use and that provided enough entertainment for most. The Link plant was closed down and the assets were liquidated in December 1930, leaving the trainer and the Link Flying School without a home.

Ed moved his ground school to the Chenango Bridge field near Binghamton. There he also serviced airplanes and gave flight instruction. He chartered flights and operated the first scheduled airline out of Binghamton. This curious development occurred when the imaginative and resourceful management of the Martz Bus Company worked out an arrangement with various pilots along its Buffalo to New York route to fly bus customers to cities not served by the firm. Ed was hired to fly passengers on a regular schedule between Scranton (which was on the bus route) and Binghamton (which was not). This operation lasted almost six months, then a shortage of customers doomed the whole scheme.

To fill the financial gap, Ed resorted to stunt flying, parachute jumping and barnstorming. He soon was a graduate *cum laude* of the rugged barnstorming school, though none of this suited him. He once commented that he disliked using airplanes for such foolish purposes. Though he excelled at the aerobatic displays that were a necessary part of the barnstormers' "come on," neither he nor the members of his barnstorming troupe enjoyed performing in this way. Often they ended up flipping a coin to see which of them would have to do the stunt routine. Ed thought of airplanes and aviation as too important to play with, and he and others were a little afraid of the airplanes at that time.

In spite of his dislike of barnstorming, Ed got more deeply involved in traveling with his little group since it did offer a way of making a living. But as he toured the country he tried to establish a new image of the pilot. He never drank, except at home, and was quiet and serious when in a crowd. He avoided boasting about his flying experiences and never told the terrifying air tales that were the barnstormers' stock in trade. He often said he wanted to promote aviation, not kill it. When he launched his first training program and was diligently trying to enroll students, he even forced himself to join various business organizations, such as the Chamber of Commerce and civic groups, an almost unheard of step for a pilot.

During the latter part of 1929, Ed's interests broadened to include a young lady, Marion Clayton. She was a graduate of Syracuse University, School of Journalism, and was, at that time, working for the Binghamton *Press*. She was the daughter of a moderately well-to-do grocer and politician in Ilion, New York. Before graduating in June 1929, she worked on the Utica paper and very briefly for one in Syracuse. Marion became interested in flying when her Utica editor assigned her a story describing a flight with the then famous Dick Botsford. In order not to frighten her, Dick gave Marion a straight and level ride. When she mentioned that flying wasn't very thrilling, he took her aloft again and did a series of loops and rolls, bringing her to the verge of airsickness. Her rueful comment was, "Dick really changed my mind fast."

Marion met Ed on a blind date arranged by a mutual friend. While groping for stimulating subjects, he told her about his dog, Pat, that liked to fly. He allowed that this remarkable beast could recognize the sound of his airplane's engine. Strange as it seems, this unlikely bit of intelligence caught the young lady's interest and a few days later, she called to arrange for an interview for an article about Ed's air-minded dog. This meeting launched a romance that has been aloft now for over forty years.

After staying at the YWCA for a while, Marion roomed in the home of a friend, Jane Reynolds, and both girls took lessons at the Link Flying School. While Marion seemed more interested in Ed, Jane soloed and obtained over twenty hours of air time before she had to stop because of the Depression. Marion soloed later, but never tried for her license. For all practical purposes, she gave up on being a pilot, but continued flying with Ed. She often accompanied him on his barnstorming trips.

By the end of 1930, Ed had over 480 hours, with 170 of these in cross-country flying. The rest were instructional, passenger hopping and various other commercial air ventures. Even Ed's mother, who had opposed his flying in the beginning, became one of his favored passengers in this period. With his earnings Ed was able to add several more airplanes to his fleet, but the pickings got leaner in 1931. Dual time instruction rates that used to be twenty-five dollars or thirty dollars per hour became ten dollars, and barn-storming rides that formerly sold for three dollars to five dollars became one dollar. The ground school training dwindled to about nothing. In quiet desperation, Ed would load his trainer on a borrowed flatbed truck and take it to fairs and amusement sites. By charging twenty-five cents a ride, he could scratch up a few dollars. The thought that people might pay to ride the pilot-maker evolved when Ed and his brother, George, took the trainer to St. Louis, Missouri, to display it in the 1931 National Aircraft Exhibit. When officials refused to enter the "gadget" as an exhibit, Ed set up his own show, selling rides for twenty-five cents. Business boomed as people lined up to experience the sensation of being at the controls of an airplane. The Link brothers' success resulted in several trainers being sold to amusement parks.

In spite of these brief successes the Depression continued to lay a pall over the Link enterprises. In defiance of his problems, however, Ed and Marion were married on June 6, 1931. Spirits improved, but not business. Marion moved right into the flying business and began doing the things that Ed didn't do well—bookkeeping, public relations and collecting money. Soon she put the Link Aeronautical Corporation, as Ed's company was now called, on a more businesslike basis and she put the school on a sounder academic footing. Marion wrote the curriculum for the Link ground school. She accomplished this by taking down Ed's dictation, rewriting it and including the finished product in textbook form. While there were many books on the adventures of flying, this was certainly one of the first books on how to fly.

Ed and Marion bravely struggled through the first year

37

of marriage, barnstorming, teaching ground school and giving flying lessons, but finally, in the summer of 1932, the company had to give up the facilities at Chenango Bridge and move to a less desirable field at nearby Endicott, New York.

While almost fifty pilot-makers had been sold for use in amusement parks, only three had been bought by the aviation industry. The first one, in 1930, went to the Pioneer Instrument Company of Brooklyn, where it was employed to demonstrate the three major instruments in use: the bank and turn indicator, the magnetic compass and the air speed indicator. Because of the trainer's 360-degree turn feature, Pioneer was able to show the need for these instruments to prevent the effects of pilot vertigo.

The second pilot-maker went to New York University's Museum of Arts and Industry, while the third was sold to the United States Navy in 1931 for use at their aviation field in Pensacola, Florida. The first two trainers, without instruments, cost $450. The Navy device, which was complete with instruments, was sold for $1500. Because they had no instruments, those trainers that went to the amusement industry sold for anything between $300 and $500. These figures merely covered the cost of making the trainer, and there was no profit.

Ed spent considerable time in Pensacola selling the pilot-maker and teaching ten Navy instructors how to use it to its fullest advantage. He was able to teach one officer, who had never been in an airplane before Ed's arrival, to fly by instruments. Officials of the Navy were deeply impressed with the trainer and made a request to Washington for five more.

In their proposed report, the base commander stated that the pilot-maker would cut the required instrument training time—which was only five hours—in half. When Ed saw this, he said that two-and-a-half hours of instrument time was insufficient, and recommended that the trainer be employed only to augment the five-hour instrument course. This was done. And when the top Navy brass in Washington saw no saving in time or money, they rejected Pensacola's request for additional pilot-makers. Thus, by his own honest appraisal of the value of instrument time, Ed lost out on the sale of five or more trainers.

While the Curtiss-Wright Company didn't purchase a trainer or a pilot-maker, the head of the flight school, Charles S. (Casey) Jones showed great interest in it. Casey was a well-known figure in aviation, having trained under Wilbur Wright and served as a pilot in World War I. He had been instructor of many of the top brass of Army aviation and well-known civilian fliers of that time, including Suzanne Humphreys; Hubert Julian, the Black Eagle of Harlem; and, Hugh Herndon, Jr., who flew across the Pacific on a round-the-world flight with Clyde Pangborn; and Warren Eaton, president of the Soaring Society of America. Casey also held the world's speed record for aircraft in 1931.

When Casey left Curtiss-Wright in 1932 to form JVW Corporation with George Vaughn and Lee Warrender, this firm operated all the facilities, including Eastern Aeronautical School, at Newark, New Jersey. This school was established the previous year by Vaughn, America's second leading ace, following Eddie Rickenbacker, in World War I. The

39

school was later called Casey Jones School of Aeronautics and is still in operation at La Guardia Airport under the name of the Academy of Aeronautics.

Casey was deeply impressed with the young man from Binghamton who could teach people to fly up to first solo for eighty-five dollars. It was costing Casey at that time over two hundred dollars to accomplish the same task. After a great deal of discussion with Ed, the JVW Corporation bought six pilot-makers. While five of these were employed for promotional activities of the school and for amusement park use, one trainer remained at Eastern Aeronautics for student training. Part of the purchase agreement was that Ed would come to Newark and set up a course of study for the pilot-maker's use.

Ed commuted between Newark and Binghamton in his airplane. After the Link operation shifted to Endicott, Marion and Ed lived in Newark for a short time. George T. Link, who had joined his brother on a part-time basis in 1929, took over the full-time job of business manager and president of the company.

Many of Ed's flights between Endicott and Newark were made in instrument flying conditions. It was Ed's skill at blind flying that impressed Casey Jones to the point where he wondered if Ed should not teach blind flying at his school. Ed explained that he could teach these skills with the help of his trainer and an appropriate ground school program and that he would be able to develop instructors for the school.

After some discussion, Ed agreed to teach one of Casey's instructors, Karl Kail, the necessary techniques. Blind flying training got under way at once, and this specialty of Eastern Aeronautics became very popular.

As Ed's efforts to sell his trainer elsewhere failed, he concluded that he must have an experienced sales force. The JVW Corporation was a natural and Casey's company became the exclusive sales representatives for the Link Trainer. This agreement, made in 1932, was verbal and existed until the JVW Corporation became inactive after World War II.

While the JVW's first-year goal of one hundred sales was unrealized, the pilot-maker received its first important aviation publicity. In 1933, the New York *Herald Tribune,* in its Sunday edition in an illustrated article, went into considerable detail in describing the Link Trainer. The *Herald Tribune* noted that a new method of instruction in "blind flying" and radio beam navigation had been developed "whereby the student is given most of his training without leaving the ground," and described its use at a Newark school, saying that "it promises to revise completely the meaning of the once disparaging term 'hangar flying,' since for the first time it affords airmen an indoor opportunity for improving their skill along other than conversational lines."

Continuing, the New York daily said:

> This system does not purport to turn out a finished "blind" flier without the necessity of actual time in the air at the controls and behind the instrument board of a real airplane, but its sponsors do claim that it will shorten the essential air training by more than 50 per cent. They maintain that 15 hours of the new style "hangar flying" and five hours in the school's blind flying training plane will result in a proficiency equivalent to that obtained by 25 hours' blind flying instruction on an all-airplane basis, which has been the average time required to qualify America's airline pilots in this highly specialized field.

Soon a new lead for sales developed when the Curtiss-Wright company allowed the Link Aviation Trainer to be exhibited in its Manhattan showroom.

At about the same time, the New York *Post* described the trainer as a "Blind Flyer Pilot-maker" and publicized Ed's claim that he could teach students to fly for only eighty-five dollars through its use.

When the Links returned to Endicott in the winter of '33, Ed found his company without a home. The city fathers decided that aviation was not a desirable business for their city, since low-flying planes of the Link Corporation could endanger the lives of Endicott's citizens. George F. Johnson, president of the Endicott Johnson Corporation, a famous shoe-making firm, had made the space available for the field on company-owned property. But, when the activity at the airport increased because of the Link operation, he threatened to revoke the city's use of the field. When Ed approached Johnson about his staying on in Endicott, the shoe magnate asked him if there were any nearby fields where he could establish his flying business. Ed said that the Cortland airport was available, but he didn't have the money to move. Johnson inquired as to moving costs and then proceeded to write a check for the full amount. Thus, the Link Aeronautical Corporation moved to Cortland, some forty-five miles north of Binghamton.

The Cortland airport had been dedicated in 1931 and had had little or no use since then. It was in a beautiful location, four miles out of town on a lovely grassy plain. Whatever possessed the city fathers to build it in the first place at a cost of almost $100,000 may never be known. But it was only one of several partial commitments to the world of aviation that was to leave this field today, except for a paved strip, very much as it was almost forty years ago.

A fine new hangar was constructed, suitable for half a dozen small airplanes, and the door was large enough to accommodate a Ford Tri-Motor, the largest plane of the day. In the back was a shed that provided room for tools and equipment to service the airplanes. It was in this building that the Link Aeronautical Corporation set up its school and shops. The monthly rental was fifty dollars and Ed was made Cortland Airport manager—at no remuneration.

The regional press noted the arrival of the new business with approval. Here is how Louis Van Dyck, editor of the Cortland *Standard,* used his editorial license to announce the big event on May 19, 1933:

Cortland airport was leased today to the Link Aeronautical Corporation, for the past six years operators of the Endicott Airport.

E. A. Link, Jr., secretary-treasurer of the company, and Lt. William J. Carroll, associated with the firm, were in Cortland today to complete negotiations and will take possession of the port at once. Ships will be sent here next week although the firm will not take full control of the port until June 1. During the week following, all equipment and machinery of the U.S. Government Approved Repair Station No. 97 will be brought here and the port will be devoted exclusively to aviation.

The repair station, which has been operated in Endicott, includes modern machine shop equipment with stock and materials for repairing and rebuilding all types of aircraft. In addition, the company will bring five ships to Cortland and within the next few months will bring seven other machines, privately owned to the Cortland airport.

THE PILOT MAKER

Lieutenant Carroll, who has made his home in Cortland for the past two years and was with the British naval air service during the World War, will be field manager of the port.

Mr. Link, who has done commercial flying since 1926 with 2,000 hours of safe flying to his credit, plans to move his family to this city at once. He will bring two men with him to be employed in the manufacture of the Link Pilot-Maker, a device which has been adopted by the naval department and is being considered for army aviation training. In addition to Lieutenant Carroll and Mr. Link, a third experienced pilot is coming here with the organization, Lt. Alfred Stanley, an American ace with eight official victories to his credit in the Lafayette Escadrille. These three pilots will handle commercial flying and the training of students, Mr. Link having soloed 91 students from the Link Flying School since it was organized in Endicott when the airport was opened in 1927. The reason that the organization is leaving Endicott is that the airport there, which has become part of a real estate development, is being converted into building lots.

The ships which the Link Corporation will bring here are: A 128 horsepower Cessna four-place monoplane powered with a Siemens-Halske motor; a five-place Fairchild powered with a Wright Whirlwind motor; a three-place Travelair biplane with the same power unit as the Cessna; a two-place American Eaglet monoplane powered with a Szekley 45 horsepower motor. This ship is used as a training plane. A fifth plane, a four-passenger Stinson Cabin Monoplane, belonging to Dr. F. J. Moore of Endicott, will be brought here also and used for passenger service.

Arrangement has been made with a local organization which has secured the use of the airport dance floor to use the hall for dances until June 3, after which time the dance floor will be removed and the aviation equipment will fill the building. The restaurant at the airport will be continued for convenience of fliers, but other amusement devices there will be removed.

44

Mr. Link plans to keep up his Binghamton commercial flying and will maintain a direct telephone wire to that city so that he will be able to send ships there on a few minutes' notice for commercial flights. He plans to continue his plan of chartering planes to any airport at any time.

By early June, Ed was ready to open up for business. The airport opening was an event in Cortland and *The Standard* discussed the planned event in its June 10, 1933 issue as follows:

Everything was in readiness at the Cortland Airport this morning for the opening of the air show this afternoon and Sunday, which will mark the formal opening of the port under the management of the Link Aeronautical Corporation.

A Pitcairn autogiro, the third one to visit the city, was reported to have left Washington, New Jersey, this morning and will carry passengers and students this afternoon and tomorrow. This will be the first opportunity for the general public of Cortland to experience the novelty of going aloft in a "flying windmill."

Parachute jumps and stunt flying will make up the program for tomorrow, while passengers will be given a wide choice in the style of plane in which they wish to ride. A balloon bursting stunt is planned by Pilot Earl Eckles with the autogiro, while Pilot Harold Bowen of the Norwich Airport will provide the stunts with his tapered wing Waco. Pilot Ed Link, who has been in Washington for the week, is back in the city, and with pilots Al Stanley and Bill Carroll, will fly the airport planes. Visiting pilots are expected here also to carry passengers.

With the weather man predicting fair weather for Sunday, a large crowd is expected to greet the new management at the airport.

There was a large crowd on opening day in Cortland. But even with a huge sign proclaiming the eighty-five-dollar learn-to-fly offer, the Depression continued to grind on and there were few takers. Barnstorming and charter flying had dropped to nothing. Marion kept books, sold tickets for air rides, transcribed ground school lessons, and, on weekends, ran a hot-dog stand at the airport. The food for the Links' dinners often consisted of what was left over from the end of the day's sale at the stand. As Ed often recalls, Marion and he lived a "hamburger and hot-dog existence."

Prospects indeed were dismal. In spite of the new President, Franklin D. Roosevelt, the Depression was getting worse. Marion was ailing with ulcerative colitis. Her father helped pay some of the doctor's bills so that Ed could keep going. His own parents had lost everything. The big family house in Binghamton was rented, and Marion and Ed were living in one room over the Cortland Tea Room, owned by the Alonzo Swartwouts. George left the company for employment elsewhere, and Ed assumed the presidency of his firm. In his frantic search to find ways to make money from his airplanes, Ed wondered if the almost automatic reaction of people to look up everytime an airplane flew over could not be put to commercial use. He began to experiment with signs which could be lighted at night to spell words. It was a weird notion, but by constructing a series of wooden frames in the shape of rectangles and then adding an X in the square and placing lights at the intersections of each angle, he found he could, by lighting the proper bulbs in sequence spell words. The idea was that if such a sign could be rigged on the underside of an airplane and flown over a city, people would be bound to look up and read it.

After much experimentation a sign was rigged under the wing of the Travelair biplane, but its engine wasn't powerful enough to haul both the craft and the sign aloft. Next Ed borrowed a Stinson monoplane with its more powerful Wright Whirlwind J-6 engine and the sign was airborne. The electric sign was equipped with seven hundred small incandescent bulbs with the electricity furnished by air-driven generators mounted on the aircraft. It was possible to display any letter of the alphabet so that a combination of words up to ten-letters long could be flashed, followed immediately by another series. The letters were seven feet high and four feet wide, and were legible at night from an altitude of 2,500 feet. A mile of wire on the plane connected the letters with the central device located in the cabin of the plane.

Ed gave a demonstration of his aerial sign to Spaulding Baking Company, and the management liked the idea. Thus, on the clear balmy night of July 24, 1933, the message, Spaulding's Cakes Are Fresher, flashed for half an hour over Cortland and Binghamton. To make certain that even the hard-of-hearing would not miss the fact that an airplane was flying over—and thereby miss the message—a siren was rigged to the craft so that it wailed as the plane crisscrossed overhead. There followed other advertisers—Utica Club Beer, Enna Jettick Shoes—and longer trips. At first, the trips were to nearby Elmira-Corning-Bath-Syracuse-Oneida areas; later, there were flights to Philadelphia, Newark and New York City.

Business started to pick up and the Link aerial advertising program was proving profitable. The firm was able to add a Ford Tri-Motor to its fleet, but there were hazards in the business, too. It meant night flying from unlighted fields and

47

flying in all kinds of weather. Of necessity, Ed and the three pilots he hired became experts at instrument flying and there was always the danger of forced landings and the attendant worry of vandalism. Here's one account of a flight as it appeared in a Camden, New Jersey, newspaper:

Souvenir hunters and other vandals completely destroyed the Fairchild cabin monoplane owned by the Link Aeronautical Corporation of Cortland after it had been damaged by a forced landing at Glenolden, a suburb of Philadelphia, Friday evening at eight o'clock.

The ship, which was being flown by Pilot George Bevans, carried an electric sky sign, an invention of E. A. Link, manager of the local airport. Mr. Bevans had gone aloft from the Camden Airport with Douglas Kline, a mechanic at the airport, as his passenger, a few minutes before, when his motor stalled.

Flying over a thickly settled area, Bevans saw only one small vacant lot within gliding distance. He side-slipped his ship down from an altitude of 1,000 feet into the small field, wrecking one wing of the plane in landing and doing some other damage to the ship. Bevans received a cut on his forehead, but his passenger was uninjured.

Word was sent at once by telegram to Mr. Link, who started from Cortland with his light truck for Philadelphia, hoping to arrive before daybreak to prevent vandalism. He was accompanied by E. B. Fish of the airport staff. Upon arriving at 7:00 AM, they found that vandals had been at work all night, wrecking the ship completely with stones and clubs, and carrying away with them valuable pieces of equipment which had escaped damage.

Bevans and Kline had fought off the vandals as long as they could, but with the large expanse of the plane, it was impossible for them to protect all sides. Finally Bevans was taken to the hospital to have his wound dressed, and he remained there for observation. A lone Glenolden policeman, a man advanced in years, spent part of the night at the scene, but could not hold back the mob of hunters who stripped and destroyed the craft. Mr. Link was able to salvage the motor of the ship and found that Glenolden firemen had rescued the radio, parachutes, flare and a few parts from the ship."

Though success seemed to be in sight for the Links, Ed's troubles weren't over. He was deeply in debt and had difficulty in raising enough cash to get material to fill his orders. One person to whom Link owed money, thinking to get a piece of what he guessed would be a good business someday, decided to attach the only asset of the Link Corporation: its airplane. Word of this maneuver reached Ed one stormy night. In spite of the weather he was determined to fly his airplane to the safety of another state. In a blinding snowstorm, he flew out of Cortland Airport on instruments, landing several hours later in Scranton, Pennsylvania. He returned the next day by train to get on with the job of building trainers. Two weeks later when cash for delivered trainers was received and debts paid, the plane was brought back safely to Cortland.

In 1934, Ed's factory was still a small area at the back of the largely unused hangar at the Cortland Airport. It was bitter cold and the only heat was from an old-fashioned space-heater. When Ed signed the five-year lease on the airport building in 1933, he agreed to pay fifty dollars a month until June 1, 1934, when his rental was to be increased to $115. But Ed understood the increase was to cover an improvement in the facilities. The Airport Board of the Cortland Chamber of Commerce then threatened to raise the ante to $250 per month.

The Board and Ed had a running battle from June to December 1934 over the size of the building, its heating and rent. At last a showdown seemed imminent. Then one day one of Ed's employees, who was also a deputy sheriff, reported to his boss that the city planned to serve seizure papers on the corporation on December 26, seeking to recover four hundred dollars it believed was due. Thus it was that with the sheriff at his heels, Ed loaded up several pickup trucks and moved everything to a small factory on Gaines Street in Binghamton on Christmas Day. Frustrated, the City of Cortland sued the Link Aeronautical Corporation. The legal battles dragged on until, on April 24, 1935, when an agreement was reached by which the Link concern paid $875 in back rent and was then freed from all obligations of its lease.

This was all forgotten, it seems, when years later, on January 26, 1958, the City of Cortland sponsored a testimonial dinner for Ed and Marion Link, and dedicated a bronze plaque at the airport which reads as follows:

EDWIN A. LINK

On this site in the early 1930's, the "Link Flight Trainer" was perfected and resulted in the first sale to the Army Air Corps of ten trainers. This heralded a new era in aviation safety and progress. During World War II, Link trainers were used to train more than half a million airmen throughout the world. The citizens of Cortland County are proud of this historic association and grateful to this inventive genius for his dedicated service in behalf of his fellow Americans.

4

Did You Get Your Link Time?

By 1934, there were also the first faint signs of improvement in the country's economic life. Aviation was beginning to prosper. Airlines sprang up around the country and fought for the right to carry mail. Since these carriers were paid by the Post Office Department at a rate far greater than the cost to the public, friends of an airline would mail each other lead weights, anchors and other small and heavy objects. In a fury the Post Office, on February 1934, cancelled all air mail contracts, and asked the Army Air Corps to do the flying.

The Air Corps fleet of fifty or so aging airplanes and twice that many pilots bravely took up the challenge. Unfortunately the pilots of that day had little experience in night and instrument flying and in the first few days, five airplanes crashed and their pilots were killed. The Corps was desperate. Embarrassed and frustrated, the Army limited flights to daytime and clear weather only while groping for a solution to the problem.

For some time, Casey Jones and George Vaughn, who

had maintained their friendship with the military, attempted to sell the Army a pilot-maker. As early as 1932 they had prevailed on Ed to loan a trainer to the New Jersey National Guard unit at Newark Airport. The trainer made such a favorable impression that one of the officers decided the regular Army should take a look and had it shipped to Bolling Field, Washington, D.C., for an Army Air Corps evaluation. While many of the officers agreed that the Army should make the pilot-maker standard equipment at all airfields, budget considerations prevailed and no orders were received. When the Air Corps encountered catastrophe in its attempt to fulfill airmail contracts, Jones quickly realized that the Army would have to train its pilots to fly on instruments and, through the help of some of his friends in Washington, arranged a demonstration of the pilot-maker for a group of Army Air Corps officers at Jones' school in Newark for February 11, 1934.

On February 10, Ed received a long-distance call from Casey requesting him to come to Newark airport the next day to demonstrate the pilot-maker to the local Army brass. The day dawned cold and foggy and thoroughly awful for flying. The Air Corps group arrived at the airport, took one look at the soupy weather, and concluded that Ed wouldn't arrive. Just as they were about to leave, however, his plane droned overhead. He had made it on instruments and the Air Corps concluded that he must know plenty about instrument flying. Highly pleased with the operation of the pilot-maker, the officers quickly reported to Washington the immediate need for Link's device, but the lack of funds blocked an order. Then Casey Jones took over. He and Ed flew to Washington to see Brigadier General Oscar S. Westover, assistant chief of the Air Corps. Although General Westover immediately recognized the advantages of the trainer, he informed them that no funds were available for an immediate purchase.

With the Army's hands tied, the two visitors then went to Congress, calling upon Congressman Howard McSwain, Chairman of the House military affairs committee. He approved of the project and got in touch with the War Department at once. He promised the cooperation of his committee in putting the funds through, empowering Major General Benjamin D. Foloise to proceed, with the assurance that the military affairs committee was back of him. An emergency appropriation was passed by both Houses of Congress and signed by the President on March 28, 1934.

When the Army took delivery of its first six trainers on June 23, 1934, simulators had made the grade and a new industry was born.

The final inspection and acceptance of these first six Link Model "A" trainers was done by June 5, 1934. Two of the trainers were shipped by boat, one going to Duncan Field, San Antonio, Texas, and the other going to March Field, California. The other four made their trip by rail to Wright Field, at Dayton, Ohio; Langley Field at Hampton, Virginia; Mitchell Field at Mineola, New York; and Selfridge Field at Mount Clemens, Michigan. The selling price of each unit was $3,400.

One month later, Link sold another trainer to Okura & Company for delivery to Japan. This proved to be the first of ten trainers that were sold to the Japanese during the next twelve months. This relationship culminated in 1935 with an invitation to Marion and Ed to go to Japan, all expenses paid, to assist the Japanese Navy in organizing a training school for instrument instructors. Ed was somewhat apprehensive about going since relations between China and Japan had deteriorated and war seemed inevitable. The State Department, however, assured the Links that it was safe to go and even encouraged them to make the trip, doubtless with an eye on the possibility of the Links returning with an insight into the political and military intentions of the Japanese.

Though harboring some reservations, Ed and Marion sailed from San Francisco and arrived in Japan ready for anything. Ed's first inspection trip of the training facility where the trainers were set up suggested the second reason for the trip. He was soon aware that one of the pilot-makers had been completely disassembled and the mechanics were obviously having trouble putting it back together. Ed felt confident that the device had been copied in every detail with a view to manufacturing made-in-Japan trainers, but there wasn't a thing that he could do about it, since no patent protection existed at the time.

His Japanese hosts suggested that they would like to have Ed direct the reassembling of the trainer spread in pieces on the floor. However, Ed declined, avowing, as was true, that he would have to have the special equipment and tools that existed only at his factory. It was, as he knew, a futile ploy, for the Japanese would sooner or later be able to manufacture the equipment necessary to put things right. The visit continued for six weeks or so until the instruction of the new class was completed and, incidentally, many long-standing business and personal friendships were established.

The next foreign order came from the Amtorg Trading

Corporation, which purchased four Model "A" trainers for the USSR. The Model "A" consisted of a dummy fuselage equipped with wings and control surfaces mounted on a turntable which in turn was mounted on a base. The cockpit was equipped with standard controls, and the instrument panel contained a compass and air speed, rate of climb and turn and bank indicators, and also the volume control for the pilot to use when flying the radio range. The radio signals were produced by the instructor and transmitted to the student to simulate signals heard in flight. Rough air could be turned on and off at the will of the pilot by a switch mounted on the instrument panel.

By this time the military had acknowledged the necessity for instrument training and orders rolled in at a steady pace. Soon, too, the rumblings of discontent in Europe prompted England and France to look to their aviation strength, and Link Trainers began to appear in the training centers of the Royal Air Force. It seemed a good time to reorganize Ed's several business interests. Ed continued the Link Aeronautical Corporation as a fixed-base operation, flight school, airplane repair service and charter operator at the newly established Tri Cities Airport west of Endicott, N.Y. A new company was then established, Link Aviation Devices, Inc., to manufacture flight training equipment. The new company soon became Link Aviation, Inc., and Ed remained as president of both companies. George Link became treasurer.

In addition to strong military orders, in 1936 the first production models of the Link "C" Series Instrument Flying Trainer made their appearance in several flying schools of the United States. They featured a full-scale instrument panel and desk assembly for an instructor. The trainer itself had the old-style fuselage with zippered access openings on the sides. The ventilating system relied on two small fans, one in the nose to bring in air and the other under the seat for an exhaust. Instruments included as standard equipment were airspeed indicator, vertical speed indicator, altimeter, magnetic compass, radio compass, tachometer, turn and bank indicator, artificial horizon, directional gyro, and marker beacon indicator. To complete the realism the panel also contained an ignition switch, rheostat controls for instrument lights, radio volume and radio compass sensitivity controls, plug-in connections for microphones and earphones, and transmitting key.

The cost of the Model "C" trainer remained between $3500 and $5500, depending on instrumentation and the inevitable refinements and improvements that were made. Shortly after its introduction a remote indicating instrument panel was added for the instructor, and new mechanisms were created to simulate the effects of wind drift. Soon more accurate radio signal information was incorporated. These and other modifications resulted in the evolution of the "D" Series trainer in 1937. Most of the new "D" trainers were shipped overseas where the European air forces were already gearing up for what would become the Second World War.

Although the instruments were largely standard, the readouts conformed with the language and customs of the country in which the trainer was located. A requirement of the contract to supply the British Royal Air Force with several hundred trainers called for manufacture in the British Empire. This led to the formation in 1937 of the Link Manufacturing Company, Ltd., at the sleepy little town of Gananoque, Canada. The site had been chosen to some degree because of its proximity to a new summer home of the Links at Perch Island in the St. Lawrence River's Thousand Islands.

By this time Ed had acquired an amphibian twin-engine Grumman Widgeon airplane with which he commuted between the plants in Binghamton and the new Canadian factory.

The combination of the riverside location of the Gananoque plant and Ed's increasing interest in his amphibian airplane was related to an indication of some interest on the part of the Navy in a trainer to introduce its pilots to the peculiarities and hazards of flying off water. Ed's predictable response to a challenge brought about the development of the "Aqua Trainer." Although never accepted by the Navy, or developed to a completely practical stage, it was a remarkable device. Essentially it consisted of a floatable Link Trainer with cockpit, stubby wings and tail set on a shaft with a hydrofoil device on it. The entire unit sat in the water and could be propelled by a small gasoline engine. In operation, the device would rise up out of the water, responding to the pilot's movements of its controls. When working properly it could stimulate the feel of a seaplane during the critical phases of leaving the water at takeoff and settling back onto the surface during landing. While the device was an astonishing achievement and made use of several new concepts, it was expensive and tricky to operate. Its use of a snorkel device on the engine, a very thin high-speed wing and a manageable hydrofoil device are all believed to be firsts. In spite of this, it never progressed beyond the prototype stage.

At about the same time Ed started development of another new device he called the Visualator. It was one of the first attempts to collect in one basic instrument most of the information necessary for a pilot to fly on instruments. Up to that point, and indeed even today, most of the instrument readings a pilot uses come from separate dials, each providing one piece of information about the airplane's attitude. This requires the pilot to constantly scan the panel checking each instrument individually and then combining the total input in his mind before a movement of the controls can be made. Ed devised a single large display that sought to give a total picture to the pilot. Airspeed, altitude, rate of climb, horizontal condition and directional stability were all pictured in one major presentation. It was a monumental breakthrough and should have gained acceptance, but it was before its time and was summarily rejected by both the military and the commercial airlines. Similar designs are in use today by the military airlines and general aviation.

With these rebuffs in mind, Ed turned his attention to improving his standard trainers. Shortly an "E" Model with minor instrument modifications appeared. This gained some acceptance in civilian flying schools. It was followed by a much more sophisticated "E" Special that was quickly accepted by the Army Air Corps and the Navy. This series represented an attempt to incorporate all of the requirements of the military services in one package. While externally it was the same stubby fuselage with wings and tail, its capability as an instrument trainer was vastly improved. Its panel was designed to represent accurately the panels of the many aircraft then in use and it offered indications for simulated ILS (Instrument Landing System) approaches. Marker beacon lights and cross pointer displays were on the panel just as they would be in an aircraft. Additionally, Automatic Direction Finder (ADF) indications could be realistically displayed as the instructor at a desk beside the trainer cranked in the appropriate information.

For the first time, too, the "E" Special began to recognize certain characteristics of an airplane beyond the elementary turning and climbing and descending. A bank now resulted in a turn and a rudder in turn banked the trainer. A nose heaviness, too, was automatically introduced during turns, and the engine instruments reflected climbing or descending. Compared to the earlier trainers the Special was a tremendous advance and the large volume of orders both from the U.S. and overseas reflected its acceptance. Link Aviation was becoming big business.

By 1940, war had started in Europe and U.S. involvement seemed at worst a remote possibility. Though military expenditures were still small there was some effort to increase the size and capability of our Air Force. Trainer production increased steadily as a result and a new factory at Hillcrest, just outside Binghamton, was activated. As tension mounted in the world scene and the United States desperately tried to maintain a neutral role, trainers were shipped to both Germany and Japan, as well as England, France and other European countries. When the bombs finally fell at Pearl Harbor, thirty-five countries were using Link Trainers to ready their armies for war.

When war engulfed the United States the entire production of the Link facilities was taken by the Air Corps, the Navy and the Coast Guard, and demands for new and even more realistic trainers were made. It became apparent, too, that there would have to be trainers reflecting the peculiarities of particular airplanes and that, if thousands of young men from every walk of life were going to be thrust into airplanes in minimum time, there would have to be trainers that could introduce student pilots to as many of the characteristics of flight as possible. To meet these needs Ed and his engineers at Link added such seemingly less important modifications as turning error in the compass and a turn and slip indicator that responded to misuse of the controls as it would in an airplane. Additions to the instructor's desk included an automatic responding pen that marked a chart showing a student's progress over the ground. This "crab" was sometimes called the most complicated fountain pen in the world.

As changes and improvements were made, it quickly became apparent that a new model designation was in order and the ANT-18 was born. This became one of the first standard military trainers and incorporated in both accuracy of movement, realism of flight characteristics and instrumentation the most advanced state of the art at the time. It was of course only the beginning. A North American Aviation single-engine advanced training plane, designated the AT-6 by the Air Corps and the SNJ by the Navy, was one of the most used and useful airplanes in the military stable. In order to get maximum utilization from this great airplane, the military services asked for a Link trainer based on this aircraft. This was the first time a trainer had been designed to reflect the personality as well as the peculiarities of a specific airplane. It also represented a new challenge in degree of sophistication, for the AT-6-SNJ was a high performance aircraft with many of the characteristics of a fighter plane.

It took about two years to design and build this new trainer, but when it was inspected by the various military services, it met every need and quickly replaced the ANT-18 as standard. It featured more than a score of engine and flight instruments, and realistically duplicated the control responses and agile performance of the AT-6. Its communications equipment reflected the radio gear available in the airplane, and with the help of the instructor at his nearby console, complete navigation problems could be flown. Radio range orientation procedures could be duplicated as the instructor would follow the airplane's progress by watching the crab indicator crawl across the chart on his desk and feed the appropriate signal to the student. As a student's proficiency increased, wind drift and turbulence could be introduced and static, such as might be encountered in flight, could be cranked into the system. Most of the radio system was designed and formulated by Gunne Lowkrantz.

Engine instruments and fuel gages worked as they did in the airplane, and the student was expected to use the power settings appropriate to his situation. Fuel tanks had to be watched, too, as though the airplane were aloft. The story is told of one student who, after a particularly nerve-racking problem found himself in his Link Trainer, far from home and over particularly rugged terrain at night, with his fuel tanks almost empty. Following good Air Force procedure for such emergencies in flight, he threw back the hood and leapt out of the trainer, breaking his ankle on the floor three feet below.

The ANT-18 was the trainer in use when I was assigned as an instructor to the U.S. Air Force Instrument Training School at Bryan, Texas. Colonel Joseph Duckworth, who was the father of the attitude method of instrument flying, was in charge. In its simplest terms, this revolutionary system of instrument flying proposed that a pilot should place his airplane in an attitude he desired and verify this situation with his instruments, rather than steer the plane in small increments by instrument reference to the position he wished to assume. Bryan, too, was the first of the Air Corps' schools to provide an integrated program of instrument training for both flight and ground instruction. Up to that point there was no standardized method of instrument instruction in the services and for most pilots, experience with instrument flying was haphazard and, in many cases, techniques were faulty. With the introduction of the Model 45 Link Trainer, it was clear that in order to get the maximum benefit from the Link Trainer, an instrument trainer instructor's course would be necessary.

The Bryan school therefore instituted, along with the instrument flying school, the first Instrument Trainer Instructor Course. The enrollees came from all over the world and returned to their respective bases as department heads. An essential part of the training included flights in a modified AT-11 twin-engined plane in which had been installed six stations for the trainees. Each station had its own instrument panel and headset so that during flight the sounds of a radio range could be heard and the airplane's maneuvers followed. Elementary as this may appear, it is unfortunately true that up to that point a good many ground school instructors had neither been in an airplane nor listened to the actual signal of a radio range.

Shortly after my arrival, I was appointed deputy commander of the ITIC and much of my responsibility was in developing a complete course of instruction. I felt it was important to adopt the same attitude system that was being used in the flight instruction to the instrument trainer. After a good deal of trial and error, we ended up drawing a black "horizon" line on the wall of the room in which the trainer stood. We would then demonstrate a maneuver to the trainees and show them at the same time what the instruments were reporting. Then the students would be asked to close the hood of the trainer and perform the same maneuvers on instruments. The system worked very well and before long a steady flow of qualified instrument trainer instructors were streaming back to their bases ready to make full use of the remarkable Link Trainer.

As our graduates got to work in the field, we encouraged them to report shortcomings of the trainer to us so that further improvements could be incorporated into a more advanced trainer that was even then being designed. I was put in charge of receiving and analyzing these suggestions and reporting them to the USAF Instrument Standardization Board, under Colonel Duckworth. This seemed to be a never ending task for the more one understood about the Model 45, the more ideas for improvement seemed to come to mind. Curiously, many of the recommendations were made under the guise of simplifying the device when, in fact, if they were accepted, most would have further complicated matters.

After reviewing hundreds of suggestions the Standardization Board settled on its requirements and these were passed on to Link. At the same time, Ed Link and his experts, Gunne Lowenkrantz, Karl Kail and others, were concerned with the development of a fully integrated airplane trainer. An analysis of accident reports showed that although instrument flying capability was improving markedly, many pilots were coming to grief by not monitoring their engine and systems instruments. Clearly what was needed was a trainer that could give a pilot practice in flying the total airplane in instrument conditions. The Model 45 was the result.

The Model 45 might be called the first of the integrated trainers. Its movements and its instruments worked in relation to each other so that when the attitude changed, airspeed, altitude and power condition changed, too. The fuel tank indicators would gradually turn to empty and the engine sound would become rough and erratic if the temperature indications were not in the green. Higher airspeeds stimulated different pressures in the controls, necessitating trim changes, and torque or Q effects could be felt at high power settings. Thus the student pilot was forced to an awareness of all aspects of airplane operations.

Ed asked the U.S. Air Force evaluation board to look at the Model 45, and Colonel Duckworth appointed Captain George Cook, now with Eastern Airlines, and Captain Roy Ferguson, now with Delta Airlines, along with Major L. L. May and me to make the evaluation. We found an enormous improvement over previous trainers but still made recommendations such as the introduction of a torque effect feel in the trainer and the desirability of making the movement of the stick and rudder in the trainer equal to the small excursions that would be used in an actual airplane.

When our differences had been resolved and the new trainer accepted, the Army designated its model the C-8 and ordered 300. The Navy ordered 600 and tagged its the 1C-A1.

One reservation I had and duly reported to the Standardization Board about the C-8 concerned its not having an actual stall feature. Unlike any airplane which, when the angle of attack got too high and the airspeed too low, would stall, the C-8 would simply not stall in these circumstances. The Standardization Board, while agreeing such a feature would be desirable, thought it would add too much to the cost and not offer enough benefit and so did not require it. Later, when I joined the Link Company, I spoke to Ed about this. I said I thought it was an important addition and believed he should go back and try to sell the Board on the need for such a feature. I was astounded to find that he agreed with me and finally decided to add the stall function to the C-8 at no additional cost, though I knew it would increase the production expense by $200.

The success of the Link instrument flying trainer prompted the development of other special use devices. There were gunnery trainers, radar trainers for night fighters and trainers to acquaint students with automatic pilot techniques. But perhaps the one that was most complex and most admired was the Celestial Navigation Trainer. Described by the Air Force as a "marvel of American ingenuity and precision, exactly duplicating every factor encountered in flying," the CNT was designed to train a bomber crew. The trainer originally got its start at the request of the British, who in 1939 asked Ed if he couldn't design a trainer that could be used to improve the celestial navigation capabilities of their crews who were ferrying "surplus" U.S. aircraft across the Atlantic to England. Such a trainer, too, could be used to improve bombing accuracy during night raids over Europe.

Ed was immediately interested in the project, for he had long had an interest in celestial navigation. He started his research by attending a special course being offered by Captain P. V. H. Weems in Annapolis, Maryland. Weems had long been recognized as the outstanding authority on celestial navigation in America, and a warm friendship soon grew between Ed Link and Weems. Together they began to design a massive trainer suitable for use by an entire bomber crew which would operate in a huge silo-shaped building. Suspended under the roof was a layout of the sky. Three-hundred-seventy-nine stars were accurately placed in the sky, permitting navigators to shoot fixes with a sextant from their station in the simulated airplane. As the trainer developed, it continued to be called a celestial navigation trainer, though it was actually becoming a bomber crew trainer. The peculiarities of our neutralist policy prevented our acknowledging this at the time, for we were not permitted to sell or ship "war material" to the combatants in Europe.

In the fall of 1941, the first CNT was ready. In spite of its complexity and size, it cost only $85,000, exclusive of full instrumentation and the silo like building in which it was to be housed. Basically, the trainer itself consisted of a large fuselage similar to that of an airplane mounted on a tall movable frame. The fuselage had positions for pilot, bombardier, navigator and radio operator, as well as an instructor.

On a normal mission the pilot flew his plane on instruments while the navigator, working from a position behind the pilot's seat, plotted position from star fixes and relayed course directions to the pilot. A dome in the navigator's station allowed him to use his sextant for shooting of any 12 of the 379 stars accurately positioned under the ceiling of the building housing the trainer. A reproduction of terrain could be flashed on a movie screen ahead of and below the trainer

66

to allow the navigator practice in picking out landmarks during simulated daylight flight. The effect of wind drift could also be simulated on the aircraft's track. At the discretion of the instructor the earth could be partially or completely obscured by the introduction of cloud cover. Similarly, the brightness of the stars could be controlled by a rheostat switch on the instructor's panel.

As the trainer approached its target, control of the airplane would be turned over to the bombardier. By use of the then highly secret Norden bombsight, the bombardier would line up on the bomb run and fix the cross hairs on the target as it passed below on the projected terrain. At the instant of bombs away, the pilot took control again and the navigator went to work plotting the course for the trip back to base.

The Link Celestial Navigation Trainer, in addition to providing an opportunity for the individual members of a bomber crew to practice their specialties, also allowed crews to develop the teamwork that was essential to a successful mission. With the pilot acting as airplane commander, the crew members could in the safety of a simulator work together in developing the close coordination that made for a sharp crew. If ragged or sloppy crew habits developed, the instructor would be quick to detect this and, by means of his "freeze" button, could stop the action at any point and review the correct procedure.

Although the LCNT was primitive in its motion system and its visual display by today's standards, it nonetheless served its users well. The British Royal Air Force reported that flying training for its bomber crews was cut by 50 per cent with the use of the Link CNT. The saving in time and money realized by the use of this and the various other Link training devices prompted one grateful customer, Air Marshall Robert Leckie, wartime Chief of Staff of the Royal Canadian Air Force, to observe that, "the Luftwaffe met its Waterloo on all the training fields of the free world where there was a battery of Link Trainers."

5
Trainers to
Simulators

By the end of World War II trainer production had reached an all time high. The "blue box" basic instrument trainers were leaving the assembly line at the rate of one every forty-five minutes, and more than five hundred of the huge silo-housed celestial navigation trainers had been produced. But with a welcome peace, there also came a swift and sudden cancellation of further orders. The assembly lines shut down and the civilian market for trainers was glutted with military surplus. For a while the Air Force kept a token force of workers busy overhauling and reconditioning the trainers it planned to keep and through the War Assets Administration it sold some trainers back to Link for reconditioning and resale to civilian flight schools. But, clearly, a new market had to be developed if the company was to survive.

It was just prior to this point that I joined the company. The opportunities for sales were to the military for specialized advanced trainers, to the airlines for instrument flight refresher courses and to the schools for use in air-age education courses. In the case of the first two markets, I brought with me a design concept that was at odds with that of the present line of Link Trainers, and with that of Ed Link himself. In my standardization board work with the Air Force I had become convinced that the motion that was being provided was incompatible with the feel of a real airplane and therefore should be done away with. As trainers were then constructed, the trainer and thus the student sat on top of a pivot point and the machine moved beneath him. His body felt a bank or climb or descent as the trainer moved. But in an airplane a perfectly coordinated turn could not be felt since there would be little change in the direction of G forces in relation to the body. To be correct the pivot point should have been around the shoulder or neck. Since this was impractical, our customers concluded that trainers should be built without any motion. That is, they should be stationary —a view that subsequently proved to be erroneous. But at the time, my task was to sell this new concept to the inventor of moving trainers.

At the time, pressures were mounting from USAF and U.S. Navy users to do away with motion in trainers. I felt our customers were right and I proposed to Ed that we develop a line of stationary machines. At least some of my concern resulted from the emergence at that time of a major competitor.

Dr. Richard C. Dehmel of Curtiss-Wright Corporation had developed a trainer without motion which used an electronic analog computer, as contrasted with our pneumatic mechanical.

The military training people seemed to welcome the introduction of a Dehmel stationary trainer with the explanation that training would be better for two reasons: First, an instrument pilot was taught that in the air he must not use his physical sense of movement for attitude reference, and, second, the G-vector would be more accurately located in a stationary trainer, assuming level or coordinated turning flight, than would be true in a trainer with motion, as in the Link. With this kind of thinking by our customers, I set out to persuade Ed to develop a stationary Link trainer.

Ed believed that motion was absolutely indispensable to the trainer. His point was that since motion was present in flying, it must be present in a trainer, even if it was not perfectly represented. He felt that if nothing else, a student must learn to ignore it. To him, a trainer without movement could not truly qualify a man to fly in an airplane with movement.

In desperation I took Ed in the field and let him talk with some of the users. I remember once setting up a meeting at Barksdale Air Force Base, which after the war was the headquarters of instrument training. Ed met the director of training, Col. Gabriel Disosway, as well as some of the instructors, and the discussion started. I thought things were going fine for a while, but soon the talk got both loud and pretty firm, and Ed was reminded of who was the customer. From Ed's point of view, it didn't make any difference. If he didn't agree with what was said, he said so. After this heated conversation and with grave reservations, Ed did agree to produce a non-motion trainer, but he didn't change his mind about its shortcomings.

We decided that with the development of our stationary trainer we should introduce full electronics into our system since it was certain that electronic computers were going to be essential to future trainers. Many of the components of our trainers were electronic, but we hadn't developed a completely electronic model up to that time. To do so starting from scratch took a great deal of corporate courage and considerable financial risk, for it was a vast undertaking. It involved making use of advanced technology with which we were not totally familiar, and one really didn't know if it would work when completed. Even if it did, one wasn't quite certain that the customer would buy it anyway.

We knew that the development of our new trainer would take at least a year and probably more and, therefore, we could expect no revenue from that project for at least that time. In order to help create a new market for standard trainers, we decided to move on what became known as the School Link Program. Ed had felt for some time that the introduction of a basic aviation trainer into high school and even grade schools could arouse the interest of young people in flying and aviation. Accordingly we had designed a simple single-place cockpit on a pedestal with minimum instrumentation, elementary radio and as few switches as possible. The controls in the cockpit were the stick and rudder and the trainer responded with movement as would be the case in an airplane. Our objective was to produce a trainer that was relatively mobile, easy to maintain and simple to operate. We dreamed of building these in great quantity and leasing them to schools at about five hundred dollars per year.

The thought behind our effort was that, although aviation might not be an appropriate subject in every school curriculum, for some schools it could be a supplementary part of many major subject areas. Aviation examples could be used either as illustrations or facts in themselves in science and mathematics. To implement such a program, however, suitable textbook material would be necessary. As we wanted airlines to participate with Link, we asked TWA, Pan American, United Air Lines and American Airlines if they would help us, and their replies were encouraging.

Next we held a series of seminars at schools and colleges for teachers at all grade levels, explaining what we hoped to accomplish and what we thought the benefits would be. We made appearances at hundreds of teacher groups, always striving to interest and to train teachers in the use of aviation materials and, of course, in our School Link Trainer. It was tough going. The schools were hesitant to use industry-produced classroom materials because it was suspected that these would have commercial taint. To many teachers the sole object of our effort was to sell our product. While it is true that we surely hoped to sell some trainers, we also felt that there would be genuine benefit from the introduction of aviation subject matter into the classroom.

We were aided and abetted during this period by the addition to our staff of Ed's half-sister, Marilyn. (Ed's father had remarried in 1923.) She was assigned to our Education Department along with Edmund Carmody, Paul Dittman, William Konicek, Norman Potter and myself. We worked under the general guidance of Philip Hopkins, the vice president who had volunteered to put Link in the education business. Marilyn was a graduate of New York University, with a B.S. Degree in Education and was particularly adept at working with teachers.

In addition to her education training, Marilyn had her commercial pilot's certificate. We were all pilots and each of us had his own idea of how she should obtain additional flight proficiency. With all the conflicting advice, it's a wonder she continued flying at all. G. W. "Slim" Emerson, a

Link vice president, was a former barnstormer and wanted her to learn some of the less formal techniques of his day, as did "Pete" Dougherty, who was then the Link company pilot. Carmody, Dittman and I were military oriented and felt a more disciplined approach was best. Of course, Ed Link was her constant mentor. Perhaps in spite of our efforts, Marilyn progressed and received the twin-engine and instrument ratings. Her flying ability gave her a unique status in the teaching community, but our School Link Program continued to meet stiff resistance. After two almost fruitless years, we agreed that Marilyn should seek a Master's Degree and gain some experience in teaching. Accordingly she enrolled at the University of Illinois, and after receiving her M.S. degree, she went on to teach in the New Jersey Public School System, and later at the University of Nebraska. She also worked part-time for the Nebraska State Department of Aeronautics as a pilot. She continued her teaching until, in 1953, she became Executive Secretary of the newly formed Link Foundation and staff assistant in Smithsonian's National Air and Space Museum.

There is an interesting aside about Marilyn winning her instrument rating, which helped us prove a theory many of us had long held. A part of the Federal Aviation Agency requirement to qualify for the test was a substantial number of flying hours and instrument instruction hours. Building up this flight time could take as long as a year, and, of course, was terrifically expensive. With Marilyn acting as guinea pig, it was agreed that Herb Chamberlain, a qualified instrument instructor and long-time Link employee would give Marilyn most of her practice for instrument approaches and her rating in our C-8 trainer. After forty hours of Link

74

time and fewer than half the number of air hours that were required, we asked the FAA to test her. The inspector agreed and even though she had never flown an actual instrument approach at the Elmira Field where the test flight was given, she performed perfectly and passed her test. Of course, she soon acquired the necessary flight hours and became an instrument rated pilot. Years later this experience, among many others, helped our argument with the FAA that hours spent in a Link Trainer could be safely substituted for flight time.

After four years of trying and with very few sales to show for our efforts, the School Link Program was abandoned. It had cost a great deal of money and taken the time and energy of a good many people, but the resistance to innovation in the school system was too great. Our product, too, was far from perfect and the cost of maintenance and shipping was too great. The only thing left to do was to back out gracefully—which we did. In retrospect, the program was probably doomed from the start. For one thing, our trainer was too bulky and difficult to handle. As a former English teacher and a pilot, I knew something about mechanics, but I wasn't an engineer. On many occasions, I would go out to give a demonstration at a school with one of the trainers. Invariably, the first hurdle to be faced was manhandling the trainer into the school building. Usually there was a narrow set of stairs to be dealt with. Then the wings had to be put on the machine, and finally it had to be leveled. By the time our program was ready to start, I'd usually be exhausted.

This was a trying time for the Link Company. With the School Link Program dead and our new electronic simulator not yet ready, our fortunes were at a low ebb. Ed decided very wisely at this point to establish a more formal adminis- tration in the company. Initially, he appointed two men in whom he had great confidence as company general man- agers, each with major responsibilities. Slim Emerson, whom Ed had brought into the company back in the '30's, was placed in charge of manufacturing. Philip Hopkins, who had handled Ed's original patents on the pilot-maker and had been associated with the company ever since, was in charge of marketing. Gunne Lowkrantz, another of Ed's close and long-time friends, was chief engineer under Emerson, and Casey Jones remained as primary sales representative under Hopkins. Ed then began to phase himself out of the man- agement of the company.

As any student of business administration might have pre- dicted, the weaknesses of a two company general managers set-up became apparent. Unfortunately, neither of the man- agers had complete authority, and they were soon stepping on each other's toes. The solution was evident, and Ed saw it was time to break up the coterie of dedicated men who had helped build the company and go outside for profes- sional management before it was too late. He was fortunate to find a man with excellent background and years of experi- ence with Union Carbide and Ansco, who was willing to take the reins of the Link Company and, in 1950, E. Allan Willi- ford was appointed general manager.

It probably came as something of a shock to Williford to find how informally Link was run. He seemed unfazed, how- ever, and soon began to install procedures typical of efficient large corporations. He realigned the current company management and brought in new managers in finance and manufacturing.

He installed a formal job classification system with salary ranges and grades related to responsibility and formed committees to establish personnel policy and operations. These steps served to bring top management together in a formal and effective way.

Many of the Link personnel promoted by Allan at this time were young, the oldest being in his early thirties. He wisely felt that Link had great personnel potential, and he elected to take men from within who knew the business and to teach them more about how a business should be run, rather than hire more experienced and mature management from outside and teach them how simulators were built. I was appointed general sales manager of the marketing department, the first general sales manager in the history of the company, since JVW had formerly been totally responsible for sales activity.

By the 1950's we were well along with solving the problems of design and construction of an electronic simulator, and were looking for orders. We knew that although the post-World War II C-8 trainer had been a great piece of equipment and had been our bread and butter for the last five years, it was on the way out. It had been the first Link Trainer to incorporate both flight and engine instruments, trim-tabs, landing-gear and wing-flap controls. With the C-8 came the early versions of the so-called Operational Flight Trainers in the form of the F8F and SNJ (U.S. Navy 1-CA-2) Trainers. These duplicated the cockpits of the F8F bearcat fighter and SNJ Texan basic trainer respectively. The great value of these trainers had often been noted and a report made to the Subcommittee of the Committee on Appropriations of the United States House of Representatives stated that:

> In one year during the war, nineteen types of Link special devices used by the Navy were estimated to have had a potential total savings of $1,241,281,400 in one year; no estimate was made as to probable savings in lives. To train a crew of eight men to operate a patrol aircraft costs $10 an hour in a synthetic trainer, as compared to several hundred dollars an hour in combat aircraft.

> At least 524 lives, $129,613,105 and 30,692,263 man-hours were saved in one year through Army Air Force use of 11 types of Link synthetic training devices. Also, the employment of these 11 devices actually freed 15,043 men for other military duties and it appears clear that synthetic training devices, as a group, have been of tremendous value to the AAF training program during the war period.

This was all very well, but it also was in the past and the rapid onrush of jet airplanes meant the end of the C-8 type trainer. We were anxious to see what there would be for us in the 1950's. We had a book full of pictures of new airplanes for which we could build simulators, using our newly acquired modern electronic A-C analog computer technology. We were pushing hard to get somebody interested in buying something. Finally, the Air Force decided that it needed an F-80 simulator and would make its selection based on competitive proposals. This turned out to be between Curtiss-Wright and Link and after a major evaluation, we won. We were back in business in a big way.

As competition grew in the trainer business after the war, the word "Link" became a problem to keep from becoming generic. Lower case L, l-i-n-k trainer departments began to pop up around the country, and we knew that if this became widespread, our name would become just like aspirin or coke. The word "simulation" was used infrequently during the mid-'40's, but came into common use when the competition between the Curtiss-Wright and Link companies began. Curtiss tried to take possession of it when we started to protect the words "Link Trainer" aggressively, but the aviation industry soon accepted the word "simulator" for all synthetic ground training devices.

Our future in the electronic simulator field was much more secure with our winning the F-80 trainer contract for the U.S. Air Force in 1949. This trainer, designated the C-11, was the first piece of ground training equipment ever built to duplicate the operation of a jet-powered aircraft. The transition from conventional piston-engined aircraft trainers to jet trainers involved more than just eliminating the motion system in the old trainer. Our engineers turned to electronics to provide the proper indications of pitch and bank, and the result was a precise mechanism in which computers and servos and amplifiers made jet flight simulators as realistic to the earth-bound trainee as was mechanically possible. But the new C-11 trainer was evolved in the belief that the pilot being trained to fly by instruments in a jet must simultaneously be totally involved with all the problems of operating his aircraft. The proficient jet pilot must know not only his radio navigation and instrument procedures, but also how to deal accurately and swiftly with emergencies. Accordingly, the C-11 was designed to include the advantages of three

79

trainers—instrument flight, powerplant procedures and radio navigation—into one.

In appearance the Link jet trainer, dubbed the "Linktronic," resembled a scaled down diesel locomotive. It was fourteen feet long, weighed 3,750 pounds, and could be disassembled into four sections, none of which was over three feet, six inches wide. Although the trainer had no motion, it provided instrument indications of flight, including 360 degree rolls about the axis. Wind forces of up to 120 miles per hour, severe turbulence and the effects of thunderstorms and electrical disturbance could be simulated.

The student's cockpit was located in the forward section of the trainer and was covered with a hood during operation. All the controls and instruments of the C-11 functioned just as they would in actual jet flight. Rates of roll, climb and acceleration were faithfully duplicated, and the controls were loaded so that pressures varied with air speed. Two feet behind the trainee, at a master console, sat the instructor check pilot. He had a duplicate set of instruments on his panel, together with a series of twenty-three lights which alerted him to any errors his pupil was making. There were warning lights for "Incorrect Throttle Setting," "Exceeding Mach Number," "Exceeding Allowable RPM," "Engine Disabled," and so on. The check pilot also had a set of trouble switches which enabled him to introduce the symptoms of engine fire, fuel pump failure, hot tailpipe, pitot and wing ice, hydraulic system failure and many other emergency conditions that might occur on a mission. As the instructor introduced emergencies, the student was expected to take the correct remedial action.

On an average flight, the student would go through his

"before take-off" check procedure just as he would in his airplane, taxi out and take off. Realism was simulated even to the whine of the jet engine. Once in the air, the pilot pointed his airplane towards his destination and braced himself for whatever problems his instructor planned to plague him with. One situation that could be presented was the indications of a higher rate of fuel consumption than was planned. The pilot would have to recognize the problem and decide whether he could reach his planned destination or would have to change course for an alternate. Or, the instructor might cause a fuel pump to fail, thereby "starving" the engine so that he could watch the pupil's air-starting procedure. On an approach to landing the instructor could cause the hydraulic system to fail. With wing flaps and gear inoperative, the student would have to lower his gear and flaps manually and make his landing.

If the student became confused, or failed to respond with the proper procedure to an emergency, the check pilot could press an "angelic" switch which would clear the board of all troubles and allow the student to start all over again. Another similar control in the instructor's console was known as the "million-dollar switch." This could be used in the event a student exceeded the load limits of the airplane. If this occurred, the student would be thrown into an uncontrollable spin, ending with a blast of a crash horn as he hit the ground. In an actual aircraft, such an eventuality would necessitate a bailout. In the C-11, a touch of the instructor's finger on the "Engine-Aircraft Reset" switch could clear up all problems and allow a fresh start.

Our efforts to build realistic trainers were seldom without irritating problems. Many resulted from the inability of various manufacturers to provide us with precise information over the full range of values. Others came from our own inexperience in this new area of simulation.

For example, the J-33 engine had flown a significant number of hours when we started on the F-80A5 simulator for the Air Force. However, when we asked at what per cent RPM thrust went to zero, the manufacturer did not have this data because it was of no significant meaning in the original design of the aircraft. We had a similar experience in determining signal attenuation for an A-N radio range. This was true in spite of the fact that literally millions of man hours had been spent by pilots flying these ranges.

Much more embarrassing were our own mistakes! In completing the first C-11 we wanted to conduct extensive flight tests of the simulator. An intricate movie camera setup was arranged to film the instruments during maneuvers. I was appointed test pilot and Bill Wood was chief test engineer. One problem that soon came up was that the engine flamed out every time we hit any measurable negative G force. We doubted this was true in the airplane and arrangements were made for me to fly in a T-33 at Williams Field. We flew two periods on rendezvous, formation and navigation without a single flameout. I returned to Link with renewed conviction that something was wrong. It turned out that one of our engineers had carelessly slipped a decimal point so that one-tenth negative G had the effect of well over one full G!

As for navigation, the automatic radio equipment of the C-11 jet trainer was far in advance of anything else in this field. For the first time in any ground training device, it was possible to give a pilot practice in the use of VHF, VOR (very high frequency omni-range) and off-course computer equipment. Facilities provided included a radio magnetic indicator (RMI), distance measuring equipment (DME), and ID-249 cross-pointer indicators for landings and take-offs. The instructor's console provided facilities for cranking in signals for two VOR stations, and necessary controls for setting in the type of station, frequency, call letters, maximum range, and approach bearing. As the student flew beyond the range of one station, he could tune to Station Number 2, as the instructor would simulate the correct information for that station, making it possible to simulate cross-country flights of more than 1,000 miles. All signal transmissions were automatic, and the instructor had only to simulate such voice communication as was called for. By means of duplicate instruments, the instructor could also monitor a student's performance during all phases of flight. A continuous record of the student's flight was maintained on an automatic recorder located on the instructor's console. This traced the path of the flight and could be used for review afterward.

The operation of the C-11 jet trainer was essentially electronic and was based upon a series of aerodynamic equations that expressed all the essentials of jet flight. A-C analog computers were designed to solve these equations continuously as their values were changed by such physical inputs as control positions, altitude and throttle setting.

The computers expressed the changing solutions in voltages, which were fed through amplifiers and servos and were finally presented to the student pilot as instrument indications, control pressures and radio signals. That is, the electronic system, which translated every act, or failure to act, on the part of the student into instrument and control responses, consisted primarily of twenty-four A-C analog computers.

The cost of building the C-11 was well over our $75,000 bid price. We hoped to make our profit on a large order. In production runs, we estimated the cost would be between $40–$50,000, which was about one-fourth the price of a single jet training plane. We figured that the operating cost of the C-11, including instructor pay, maintenance and overhead, was about fifteen dollars hourly. By comparison, an hour's flight instruction in a small T-33 jet was close to five hundred dollars.

As is often the case with a new product, we had trouble getting the C-11 prototype perfected and finally we decided to ship the nearly completed trainer and work out the final bugs later. I went along to supervise the evaluation. As we got into the testing, we found some curious things. For example, we had installed a new instrument called an ID-48. We had been told how it should work and we had our computers built to make the instrument respond that way. When we got the instrument installed, however, the needles moved backwards. We worked for weeks on this. Finally, in desperation, W. W. Wood, Jr., project manager and later president, got a blackboard and began to analyze the problem by going through a logical series of steps. The result shocked but gratified us, and brought to light the value of our simulator. We proved without question that the instrument was incorrect, and not the simulator. The instrument was returned to the manufacturer and it was found that the gear-

The original Link Trainer. Serial number is that of Ed's first airplane.

One of the first classes of the Link Flying School in which Ed's invention underwent its initial training tests. Mrs. Link—second row, second from the right—was enrolled in the class.

The second Link Trainer ever built now resides in the Smithsonian Institution. Examining it during ceremonies celebrating twenty-five years of simulated flight (1954) are Rear Adm. Luis de Florez (in cockpit), E. A. Link, C. S. (Casey) Jones, and Rear Adm. C. T. Durgin.

Ed helps his wife Marion aboard his airplane, a Cessna C-1, in 1931.

A group of early fliers: (left to right) Father Walsh, Charles A. Lindbergh, Richard Bennett, Major J. Lamphier, and Ed Link. Col. Lindbergh's son, Jon, is now connected with Ed in his undersea operations.

The Link illuminated sign developed by Ed for aerial advertising. The airplane is a Ford Tri-motor.

The early Link Trainer production line showing assembly of the first production run of the instrument flight trainer.

The first Link instrument flight trainers to be delivered to the Air Force (then the Air Corps) as they appeared on the final inspection line.

The famed "aqua-trainer" being readied for lowering into the water. This trainer, while it was never accepted by the armed forces, was successful and was later called the "hydro-trainer."

Famed aviatrix Amelia Earhart flies one of the earliest Link Pilot-Makers, which, in the early '30s, was still looked upon as an amusement device.

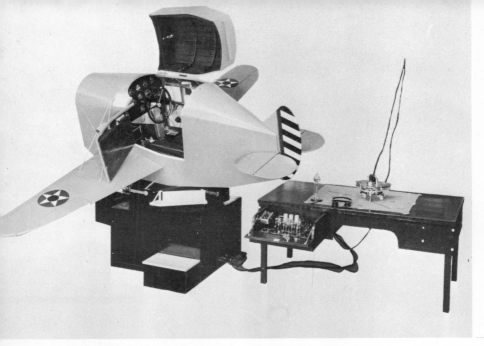

The Model E instrument trainer was produced in the mid-30s.

The famous AN-T-18 instrument trainer was the workhorse of World War II. Over half a million pilots received training in this basic instrument trainer.

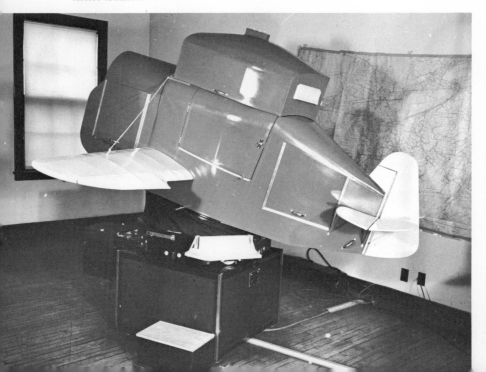

The 1-CA-1 trainer featured an automatic radio range system shown on the instructor's desk.

A crew of Link field servicemen flies a training mission in the celestial navigation trainer as part of an in-plant course of study.

The E-26 flexible gunnery trainer provided training in the handling of modern airborne gun sighting equipment.

At peak capacity Link shipped 80 trainers a week. Below is assembly line in 1945.

The 1-CA-2 flight trainer and the cyclorama.

Marilyn C. Link explains basic principles of the first School Link Trainer to a student.

The electronic SNJ-OFT duplicated the engine, flight, and radio systems of the Navy SNJ training aircraft.

The C-11B jet flight trainer, the first standard basic jet trainer for all branches of the military, was produced in the early 1950s.

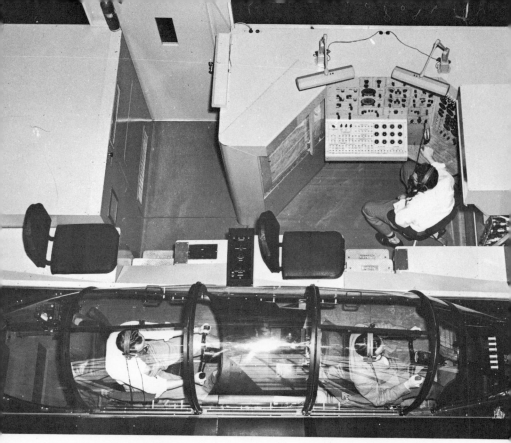

The B-47B flight simulator marked the first simulation of a modern jet bomber. It duplicated the six-jet Boeing B-47B stratojet.

The F-4C Weapon System Trainer was the first in the F-4 series.

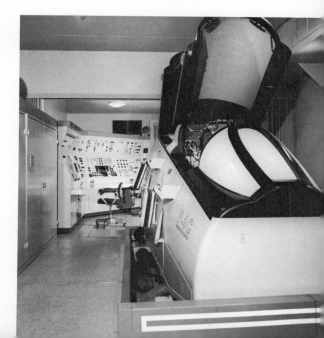

Maj. John Prodan (in pressure suit) and Col. Charles E. ("Chuck") Yaeger, Aerospace Research Pilot School Commandant, Air Force Flight Test Center, Edwards AFB, California, chat while waiting for space flight simulator to be brought into boarding position. (*Courtesy U.S. Air Force*)

The Link helicopter trainer, utilizing an actual Bell H-13 helicopter cabin, undergoing final flight tests

The simulator "flight line" at the Kirkwood Plant in Binghamton, New York.

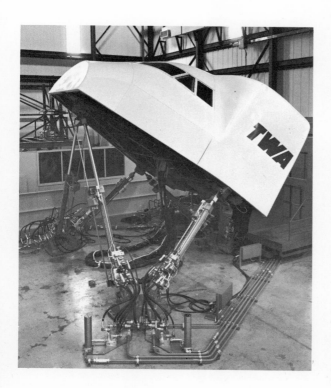

The motion system of the 747 flight simulator.

A pilot handling
the controls in a 747
flight simulator employing a
VAMP visual system.

The present-day School Link (GAT-1).

The driver trainer in use in a classroom.

Observed by the instructor, a prospective engineman is provided with a realistic exposure to locomotive operation by the Link simulator.

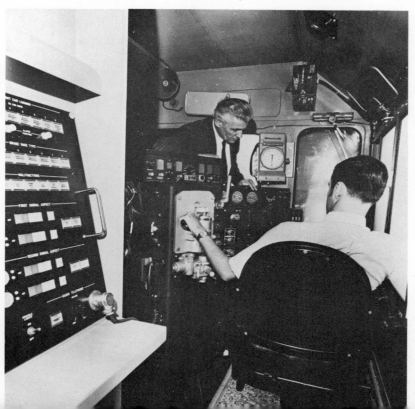

The Apollo Mission simulator.

Ed Link aboard
the *Sea Diver*.
(© *1963 National
Geographic Society*)

ing was incorrectly installed. The change was made and the C-11 accepted.

After acceptance of the first C-11 or F-80A5 trainer in 1949, the time came for a real pilot to fly it. Major Richard L. Johnson, who at that time held the world's speed record, was invited to do the honors. I was elected to be his instructor and to occupy the instructor's position in the trainer.

I had my little speech to this famous man rehearsed, and was about to welcome him when he came charging into the room, whipped off his Air Force blouse, and bounded in the cockpit almost before I could say that my name was Lloyd Kelly and I was going to tell him about the trainer. As he strapped himself in, he looked at the trainer and realized it was an F80A5. He zipped through the starting procedure and it lighted up just right. He looked satisfied. I, meanwhile, was trying to let him know that there was no external reference possible with this trainer because everything was instrument internal. Very few people had flown jet airplanes at that time with such a complete degree of reduced visibility, and we had found that most pilots who were not experienced with this tended to roll over on their back and "crash" right after takeoff. As this trainer had no motion, one couldn't sense it physically, but one could read it on the instruments. Of course, one found out there was something seriously wrong when the crash horn blasted in one's ear at the instant of ground contact.

Major Johnson rammed on the power and took off. I didn't have a chance to explain anything. As he lifted off, he radioed that he liked the airplane. Then at fifty feet, he rolled on his back and crashed. The horn went off and a red light came on indicating he was dead. Slowly, the hood was pushed back and Johnson climbed out, dazed and deafened by the blasting horn. After he recovered, I explained the trainer to him and he tried it again, this time with a little more respect. In time he became a strong booster of simulators, especially after showing me what a real T-33 would do at altitude.

A substantial order for C-11's followed its acceptance and Link Aviation entered a new period in its corporate position. Financially, we were more sound than we had been for many years. Our management was experienced and our engineering and technical personnel were the finest in the field. At the same time, it was apparent during the development of the C-11 that for the first time people other than Ed Link himself were making major contributions to the growth of the company. The new technology that went into the C-11 found people like Paul Vermont, Dr. John Hunt, Merle Crabbe, Warren Morgan, Al Decker, Bob Smith, and R. S. Neiswander becoming increasingly important. They were the ones who worked on the design and development of our electronic computers and were essential to the ultimate success of our sophisticated trainers. We were becoming a company with team skills, as contrasted with the old days when Ed built many of the trainer parts himself.

Ed recognized this change in the company and also believed in order to take the next step in the growth of Link and assure its survival in an increasingly competitive world, a merger was necessary. After discussion with several suitors over a three-year period, Ed and General Precision Equipment Corporation came to terms in 1954. There was some apprehension about how Link as a company, and many of us as individual employees, would survive the merger, but

Williford remained as president of the Link subsidiary and Ed and George Link went on the board of directors of the parent company, and all was well. There were a number of reorganizations during the next several years within General Precision, culminating in 1968 with a merger with The Singer Company.

Shortly after 1954, Ed, convinced that his company was in good hands, gradually withdrew from the business—except for one brief period in 1957 and 1958 when he took over as president of General Precision—and retired. Retired, that is, to another career which involved his interest and talents just as aviation had in earlier days.

In retrospect it seems likely that the seeds of Ed's new career were lying dormant during most of his years in aviation and at the time of his retirement, they blossomed into a new and vital interest. Perhaps it all started back in 1938 when Ed and Marion Link bought a summer home on Perch Island in the Thousand Islands of the St. Lawrence River. Here Ed's family could vacation summers and Ed could enjoy some time with them as the Link Canadian factory was located in nearby Gananoque, Ontario. Ed's amphibious Grumman Widgeon airplane was used for commuting to Perch Island from Binghamton and for extended flights into the Canadian bush country after World War II. The one shortcoming of these vacation trips to the Canadian fishing lakes was that there was no boat or canoe that could be stored in the airplane and, of course, none was available at the remote lakes. True to his fashion, Ed decided to invent portable sectional canoes and boats. In short order, Link Aviation had a marine division manufacturing the Linkboat and Linkanoe. These were easily disassembled to fit and stow into two zippered bags, each the size of a large suitcase to fit in a car trunk as well as an airplane. They were the perfect answer to Ed's problem, but they didn't seem to meet the needs of many other boaters and fishermen, for sales soon languished and the Link Marine Division in Binghamton collapsed shortly after its founding in 1949, though the Canadian Link factory manufactured and sold conventional small fishing-type boats for several years.

Also during the period after World War II, Ed had purchased a 43-foot yawl, named the *Blue Heron,* and enjoyed sailing and racing it in the waters around Florida, Cuba and the Bahamas. If at first this was like a new toy, it shortly became a new set of challenges for Ed to master. Applying the principles learned in air navigation to off-shore navigation, using air navigation charts, a radio direction finder and assembling a good crew, he felt that he had learned enough about the intricacies of yachting to enter the *Blue Heron* in the then-famed St. Petersburg–Havana race. As the starter's gun sounded and the cluster of yachts swept south, Ed's craft sailed serenely west. After the first day, there was no sign of *Blue Heron.* The Coast Guard considered sending search planes to look for the stray. They could have saved themselves the worry, for well ahead of the other racers, Ed skipped into Havana Harbor as winner in his class and second in the fleet—to the astonishment of the Race Committee. Ed had, it was learned later, used aviation weather forecasts to obtain a much broader picture of conditions than just local marine weather information. He had sailed west to pick up a sweeping wind that took him in a broad semicircle to his destination well ahead of his rivals.

A few years later, in 1951, Ed and Marion were aboard

the *Blue Heron* in Florida, ready to start on a cruise to the Bahamas, when a friend mentioned that several shipwrecks off the Florida Keys had been recently located. Ed, who had been doing some diving with air breathing equipment listened enthusiastically to the possibility of discovering ancient cannons, coins and silver bars. Accepting the invitation to join the expedition to explore these shipwrecks, the Links became treasure hunters almost overnight, scudding about the Caribbean and bringing up pieces-of-eight, ballast and other relics. Ed soon learned that the *Blue Heron* was much too delicate a craft for the heavy work required to salvage cannon, anchors and ancient spars, so he sold the faithful *Heron* and bought a sixty-five-foot converted shrimp boat. He further modified this to his needs and named it *Sea Diver*. In this rugged boat, after numerous expeditions in the waters of Florida and the Bahamas, he discovered an anchor off the coast of Haiti which may have come from Columbus' flagship, the *Santa Maria*. He then went after a Spanish treasure ship in the dangerous reef-filled waters of Silver Shoals, but he returned from this venture empty handed.

In probing further into the lore and legends of Columbus' voyages, Ed and Marion were soon at odds with many of the accepted theories about the site of Columbus' first landfall. The noted naval historian, Samuel Eliot Morison, was certain that the Great Navigator had made his first landfall in the New World on Watling Island (since officially named San Salvador) in the Bahamas, an event commemorated on Watling with a monument. Ed questioned this theory for several reasons, among them that there are no islands before Watling on which Columbus could have seen a light from far out at sea, and no cluster of surrounding islands—characteristics recorded by Columbus in his diaries about the spot where he made his original landing.

Ed set out to investigate these discrepancies with his usual persistence. Marion spent weeks in libraries pouring over ancient charts. The Links sojourned in Spain and Cuba so they could talk with Spanish historians. "I found out," Ed says, "that no one even knew what a league was in Columbus' day—it could have been one mile or three. It seemed to us the only way to prove anything was to sail the islands at the same speed we calculated that Columbus did, checking the time elapsed, as Columbus recorded it, against our own, and against the landmarks Columbus saw." Ed scouted the area in his amphibious Grumman Widgeon, and sailed, in *Sea Diver,* all possible routes, finally deciding that Columbus had landed not on Watling, but on Grand Caicos, to the southeast. The Link theory, published by the Smithsonian Institution in 1958, caused anguished shouts from Watling with its monument, but Ed sticks by his conclusions and many historians are with him.

Perhaps more important to Ed and Marion Link than the discovery of what they considered to be correction of a historical error was the discovery during their treasure hunts of a new world to be explored. Undersea exploration became their way of life and as was his wont, Ed decided that if it was to be done at all, it should be done properly. For many months he had been designing in his mind the perfect boat for his purposes. With most of the specifications set, he paid a visit to the Quincy Adams shipyard in the Boston area and ordered construction to start on *Sea Diver II*. "My aim," says Ed, "was scientific self-sufficiency." Virtually unsinkable because of its steel double hull, *Sea Diver* has a range of 7,000 miles. Equipped with a fresh water plant tapping the sea, and cavernous food storage space, including two large freezers means that *Sea Diver* can stay out of port as long as fuel lasts.

Sea Diver's broad afterdeck is capable of taking Link's amphibian, and small submersible vehicles. The *Sea Diver* can turn in its own length—an invaluable ability in coral waters and for docking—made possible by high velocity water jets in the bow. The pilot house has virtually everything an ocean liner has: radar, fathometer, sonar, loran, echo-ranging depth finders, automatic pilot and long-range ship to shore radios.

Ed describes *Sea Diver* as a workboat, and, though he is a member of the New York Yacht Club—which entitles him to use yacht club facilities anywhere—he has sometimes been waved away from famous yacht clubs because attendants think his craft is not worthy of their berths. On such occasions, Link leads his tormentors aboard and points out a full electric galley with a dishwasher and freezers, a washing machine and drier, a cherry-paneled salon that has a wood-burning fireplace, and four heads—each with a shower. *Sea Diver* has six cabins, sleeping thirteen, and the bunks are another Link innovation. Against the protest of the fitters, he had half of them installed at right angles to the sides of the ship, instead of parallel, as in other vessels, so that the sleeper wouldn't be tossed out of bed when the boat rolled. Ed and his guests say that the arrangement works well.

Sea Diver, however, is primarily a research vessel. She carries a nineteen-foot auxiliary craft, *Reef Diver,* equipped with a water-jet engine that eliminates the need for a propeller and permits *Reef Diver* to negotiate shallow reefs. In the stern, *Sea Diver* has a special watertight compartment that opens just above water level so that divers can slip directly into the sea.

Sea Diver is equipped with probably the most advanced underwater equipment in the world, much of it designed by Ed. There is a ten-inch diameter airlift—an underwater vacuum cleaner used for clearing sand from around buried undersea objects. There are pneumatic tools and complete dredging gear. There is a Link-invented underwater metal detector so sensitive that it can pick up buried tin cans. It, however, has been used for more practical purposes and has detected, for instance, objects which turned out to be tiny bronze figurines from a wreck site off the coast of Sicily.

While exploring the harbor of the Roman port of Caesarea in Israel, he found a commemorative medal nearly 2000 years old, depicting how the ancient port once looked. In the Sea of Galilee, Ed brought up the only unbroken 1st Century, A.D., Roman pottery of its kind ever found, as well as other unique pieces. Link's excursion, said a specialist, laid the basis "for Israel's greatest archaeological expedition of all times."

Scholars have long known that the sea bottom is the world's largest museum because preserved there are those objects from the past which have largely disappeared on land. Undersea archaeology may triple man's knowledge of the past, one authority estimates, and Ed has contributed through his technical ability to get down and search efficiently for this archaeological treasure. But still not satisfied, he is now concerned with the most difficult problem of all: how to keep divers down long enough, and at great enough

92

depths, to do important work in the sea—fish farming, oil drilling, and discovering new fields for scientific exploration.

"This project," he wrote in a 1962 newsletter that he sent to his friends from *Sea Diver*, "has an ultimate aim enabling man to live in the water at depths and periods of time not even considered feasible today and certainly not considered safe. Eventually, by using mixed gases, it is quite possible that depths of 1,000 feet and perhaps more can be safely attained by man for time periods that are long enough to permit useful work schedules."

Ed's solution to nitrogen narcosis was to use a helium-oxygen breathing mixture which had been tried for diving before, both by the U.S. Navy and by Hannes Keller, a Swiss mathematician, but Ed was the first to use the helium mixture both at great depths and for long periods of time.

"I'm my own captain and chief diver," Ed says. "I wouldn't ask anyone to do a dive until I've tried it myself, or tested the equipment to be used. My approach to experimental situations is to nibble away at a problem until I understand it fully. I read, ask questions, pester people. When I feel I've mastered it, I try to figure out its limits. I pass those limits only when I feel it is safe to do so."

He thought he knew those limits when he went down in his first test-dive in a Link-designed diving cylinder. This unique device of aluminum is thirty-seven inches in diameter, eleven feet long and divided into two compartments, the main chamber and an airlock. (The cylinder descends into the water vertically.) There are three hatches, one of which is on the bottom and can be left open when the capsule is down so that the diver can get in and out, the pressure inside keeping out the sea. Experimenting on this test dive, Ed did

93

not properly close the hatch. Consequently, as the capsule went down the pressure of the descent forced water to enter the capsule enough to tip the weight balance. The cylinder plunged to the bottom with water rising to Ed's neck. He got out of this scrape by turning up the pressure, but he turned it too high so that the capsule shot to the surface "like a missile from a Polaris submarine," Ed says. The cylinder released part of its air on surfacing and started down again, but this time Ed got the hatch closed and his ballast corrected. "If it had been deeper water," Ed says, "I could have drowned."

Later in that summer of 1962 Ed stayed down eight hours at sixty feet, breathing a helium oxygen mixture of gases, setting a record for a stay at this depth. He wanted to do the next step himself also—a two-day dive at 200 feet, but a Navy doctor sent to assist in the experiment told him he was too old. "I didn't think so," Ed says, "but maybe he was right and, anyway, I didn't think I should hog all the glory."

It turned out that the new record-breaking dive was made by a Belgian, Robert Stenuit, who also had something of a close squeak, but for a different reason. Stenuit was living happily in Ed's "house in the sea," as the newspapers called it, his meals sent down in pressurized containers. Every now and then he would duck out to swim about on the bottom, again breathing helium-oxygen. A strange aspect of helium is that, because it is a lighter density gas than nitrogen, the voice of a person breathing it comes out as an unintelligible chirp. Stenuit communicated with the surface by syllables— "No" (one syllable) and "Okay" (two). From below, Stenuit said "Okay," but above things were far from okay.

A storm had come up, capsizing Ed's *Reef Diver,* which was carrying a supply of helium from the pier. Stocks left on board were limited and Link had to bring Stenuit up immediately and begin decompressing him inside the chamber. The helium lasted, but just barely, until decompression was complete on that eventful day of September 10, 1962.

"He stayed down at 200 feet for twenty-four hours, fifteen minutes," Ed says, "with no ill effects. He could as easily have stayed a week. We proved our point. We proved it again the next day when, using the cylinder, we raised *Reef Diver* from 240 feet down, deeper than the *Andrea Doria* is."

Originally, Ed had planned to work with Jacques-Yves Cousteau, on a project in which two men would live far down in an underwater house with Ed's cylinder functioning as an elevator. Cousteau, however, went ahead on his own, building a house in the sea at thirty-three feet in which two men lived a week, breathing ordinary air. Later a sober scientific magazine didn't believe Cousteau proved anything and said that "Ed Link is the true pioneer of underwater housing."

After that first dive the practicality of the concept was proved, but the long hours necessary to return the human body to the surface environment through decompression troubled Ed. He reasoned that if a temporary house could be established at a work site and divers lived there for several days, working and resting by shifts, the decompression time could be reduced to the single time the diver returned to the surface, instead of having to spend long hours decompressing after each dive.

With the tragic disappearance of the nuclear submarine

Thresher in the spring of 1963, Ed was called upon to become a member of the prestigious D.S.S.R.G. (Deep Submergence Systems Review Group) formed by the U. S. Navy to investigate the loss of the *Thresher* and to make recommendations for handling future emergencies of the same kind. Consequently he sailed *Sea Diver* to the Washington Naval Yard where it remained for the balance of the year while he attended the Group hearings and work sessions, at the same time supervising the development of plans and equipment for the next dive to 400 feet, the second stage in his Man-In-Sea program.

It was Ed's belief that in order to explore and develop the continental shelves, man must be able to get about in the deeps without being confined in sealed chambers. Until then man had been able to reach these depths only in this way, with limited visibility and the handicap of working only by manipulating awkward exterior mechanical arms. To Ed this approach was unnecessarily expensive, inefficient and unacceptable.

In the spring of 1964 Ed told me, "If a man can live and work 600 feet under the sea, he can conquer a frontier as big as the African continent and as rich in oil, minerals and food." He made this statement three weeks before he headed for the Bahama Islands in *Sea Diver* to carry out the next step in his Man-In-Sea program.

For two days and nights, under Ed's watchful eye two divers ate and slept and worked on the bottom, 430 feet below the surface. The divers, Stenuit and Jon Lindbergh, were lowered to the bottom in the same aluminum chamber pressurized to the 430 feet depth. They wore suits made of foam rubber and latex, the cells inflated with compressed air.

On the bottom they lived in an inflatable rubber house about nine feet by four feet equipped with bunks, communications facilities, food and its own breathing gas supply. Ed and other experts on the deck of *Sea Diver* watched on closed circuit television as the divers swam outside to explore the sand and coral bottom and take pictures. (In conjunction with closed circuit television, Ed, along with co-inventors Gunne Lowkrantz and Karl Kail, of the Link Company, received a patent in 1960 for underwater television propulsion apparatus.)

Both dives were enthusiastically supported by the National Geographic Society and the United States Navy and its Experimental Diving Unit. Following the success of the second dive, in January of 1965 Ed persuaded two major corporations to join forces in forming a new company, Ocean Systems, Inc. Union Carbide Corporation and General Precision Equipment Corporation (now a part of The Singer Company) thus became two of the first investors in the commercial possibilities of undersea services. To date Ocean Systems has done work for oil companies drilling in deep water, for the U. S. Navy, and for others needing the services of experienced men who can operate quickly and efficiently in the ocean deeps.

The work of Ocean Systems also continues to be research oriented. Shortly after it was founded, diving history was made in Tonawanda, New York, when two divers performed the longest and deepest simulated dive ever accomplished by man. These two pioneers lived for more than forty-eight hours in a tank pressurized equivalent to what man would encounter at a depth of 650 feet.

With proof that man could survive safely for extended

periods in deep water, Ed realized that the next important step was to devise a means of transferring his human fish from the surface to the ocean bottom in comfortable and safe quarters that would also provide the mobility to carry them from one work site to another. This meant a miniature submarine. In 1966 Ed announced he had joined with John Perry, Jr., of Riviera Beach, Fla., to design and build a suitable underseas vehicle to meet the needs of a new breed of ocean explorers. Perry had been experimenting with small submersibles for some years, but the PL-4, named *Deep Diver,* which resulted from their collaboration, was the first small sub with a pressurized chamber allowing divers to leave and return underwater. The new sub was 22½ feet long and weighed 8½ tons. It cruised up to three knots under battery power, and could stay down for up to twenty-four hours.

It carried four, the pilot and observer in the forward chamber, and two divers in the center area from which they could emerge through a bottom hatch after raising the interior pressure to that of the outside ocean. The divers can move about using normal underwater swimming and breathing gear and when their work is finished, return through the hatch and begin decompression while the sub returns to the surface. For extended decompression periods, the *Deep Diver* can be lifted on to the ship's deck and the diver transferred to a larger and more comfortable chamber to complete decompression. *Deep Diver,* meanwhile can return to the work site with additional divers.

For Ed's part then this was the way vast areas of ocean could be explored. He was willing and eager to expand his interest in underwater exploration even beyond that which the more conservative members of Ocean Systems felt was in order. Through his own company, Sea Diver Corporation, he is now building a new and more radical submersible and has established Marine Science Center, Inc., just north of Fort Pierce, Fla. He started to design and build the new model in the basement of his Binghamton home. At first glance the new sub resembles a helicopter as much as anything else, with its huge see-through acrylic bubble, aluminum chamber for two or three divers, and long thin after-structure. The bubble, however, unlike a helicopter, is of four-inch thick moulded plastic and will afford a clear view of the surroundings for pilot and observer. The size and capacity of this new submersible will be about the same as its predecessor, twenty-two feet long. It will be more maneuverable, however, and be able to stay underwater for a longer period of time.

Although Ed Link still retains his pilot license and flies his amphibious airplane whenever time and the occasion warrant, his interest in aviation has waned as his deep commitment to oceanology has waxed. True, he has maintained an abiding interest in the problems of air traffic control and the need for modernizing the system by which airplanes can be guided swiftly and safely around the country without the delays and deviations that characterize so much of airline and business flying today. Many of the proposals that provided the foundation of a major two-part article in the January and February 1968 issues of the well-known aviation publication, FLYING, were based on Ed Link's ideas.

But for practical purposes, Ed has retired from aviation and gone on to a new world. When asked about this, he thoughtfully replies that for him much of the attraction of oceanology is that it is in about the same stage as aviation was when he started in it. "So little is known about the potential, yet it is bound to be enormous," says Ed. "Unquestionably, the ocean can provide food for millions. And minerals worth millions of dollars lie just a few hundred feet below the surface. Before a decade has passed," says Ed Link, "I am certain it will be commonplace for men to live and work for extended periods in the ocean. They will search for minerals, drill for oil, repair cables and run fish ranches. Tomorrow's underseas farmer will wear an aqualung and spend weeks at a time living in an undersea house. Before I'm through," continues Ed, "I hope to reach 1,000 feet down, maybe more, and live there for a while. As far as I'm concerned, the sea is the last great unexplored frontier on earth. Although I'm glad I was in aviation when I was, I'm happier still to be a part of ocean exploration now."

6

The Age of
Sophistication

Link delivered almost one thousand C-11's to all branches
of the military. Undoubtedly the most universally accepted
all-electronic trainer, the C-11's are still being used by the
United States Air Force, Navy, Coast Guard and by various
foreign countries which received them under the Mutual Defense Assistance Program (MDAP). This completely electronic simulator is generally credited with providing the
technological foundation on which all of today's jet aircraft
trainers are built.

While the C-11's were rolling off the line, Link engineers
were at work on two specialized trainers to duplicate the
Navy's F3D and SNJ-5 aircraft. The F3D was a twin jet
night fighter with a crew of two, while the SNJ-5 was the
wheelhorse of the Navy's basic air training program. Both
of these ground-bound Links were electronic throughout,
and both were "operational" in that they contained controls
and instruments duplicating those in the aircraft and functioning exactly as they do in the air.

While the SNJ-Link bore considerable physical resemblance to its airborne counterpart, the F3D Link was self-

contained within a huge trailer. Completely air-conditioned, the F3D Link was used as a mobile training installation or could be removed from the trailer in which it was housed for permanent or carrier-based operations.

Utilization of the F3D in the Navy's jet fighter training program covered every phase of flight instruction, including cockpit familiarization, ground and air engine operation, power settings and attitudes for varying conditions of flight under day and night instrument conditions. It also provided exercises in crew coordination between pilot and radar operator. The trainer could be used for transition training of new jet pilots, as well as increasing the proficiency of experienced ones.

Flight instruction and practice in the SNJ was equally complete. Training effectiveness of the SNJ was enhanced by dual instrumentation in the instructor's cockpit. For the first time in a flight trainer, the instructor actually "flew" with the student pilot and was able to "take over" whenever the occasion demanded.

In both the new trainers, a "flight" demanded all the care and skill needed in the actual aircraft. The trainers were realistic, even to sound effects. In the SNJ, a starter whine similar in tone and pitch to that of the inertia starter of the real SNJ, was heard when the starter button of the trainer was pressed. Pressure on the gun trigger switch of the control stick produced a machinegun effect. Visual and environmental effects, too, were incorporated under the double hoods of the trainers. Overcast conditions were simulated by a cloud projector and it was even possible to duplicate storm conditions, including heavy rain, static and lightning.

Our success with these super trainers helped win us in

1951 the then largest simulator contract ever awarded. This was a $6,000,000 Air Force contract calling for the development and production of trainers for the F-89D jet aircraft. The F-89D Scorpion was an all-weather interceptor built by Northrop. It required a crew of two and called for the highest degree of piloting skill and teamwork between the pilot and his radar observer.

Link's ground training version of the Scorpion was to be capable of training pilot and radar operator simultaneously, with emphasis on necessary teamwork. Its crew positions were exact copies of those in the plane. During simulated cross-country flight, weather problems could be introduced to test the pilot's ability to perform his mission under the most adverse conditions. At any time during such a flight, a target simulating an enemy aircraft could be introduced to provide practice for the radar operator to detect, track and destroy the enemy.

The fire control system of the F-89D flight simulator reproduced the "X-ray eyes" of the Scorpion. In this electronically computed and activated system were the synchronized radar scopes for the pilot and radar observer with duplicate scopes for the instructor as well. The primary instrument in the radar operator's cockpit was his radar scope. Through it, target planes were found and intercept courses established. Equally important was the pilot's scope, which supplied him with necessary information to guide the aircraft throughout the attack phase of an intercept. Signals told him when to press the trigger and when to break away. A warning light flashed to tell him when his rockets were fired.

Using automatic target programming, it was possible to run ten different problems for each target from a single tape.

Scoring equipment recorded time on track, time on search, and the number of hits and misses. The system could also simulate interference-clutter, jamming, noise, ground return and low voltage effect.

In addition to its complicated radar simulation, the Link F-89D flight simulator was equipped to teach jet pilots the procedures and techniques of flying the F-89D jet aircraft on tactical missions or training flights. Link engineers worked to rigid specifications in providing the most accurate and realistic reproduction of the flight performance of the actual aircraft in the F-89D flight simulator. So close was this duplication that for practical purposes the simulator could have been flown by following the aircraft flight instructions in the F-89D pilot's operational handbook.

Airplane feel was given special consideration in the development of the Link F-89D. In an effort to make this important aspect of pilot flight training real to the pilot, Link engineers designed and constructed a special analog computer to translate aircraft flight data into terms of dynamic response equal to actual rolling, pitching or yawing disturbances. These responses, more rapidly and more accurately determined through the better resolutions of the computer, were so precise that handling the F-89D flight simulator was very close to handling the F-89D jet fighter itself.

In normal flight the simulator matched the aircraft in performance and speeds. It climbed as fast, flew at the same speeds, and reacted to control pressures the same as the plane. Thrust and drag effect were realistically presented as were altitude effects on aircraft performance and fuel consumption rate. There was high and low speed buffeting, indicated through actual vibration of the seat, when maximum allowable airspeed or Mach number was exceeded or when the plane approached a stall. The simulator could detect when fuel distribution became unbalanced or there was a shift in CG.

It seemed that each successive trainer we built included more accurate representations of the airplane it was copying. But just as it appeared we had reached the ultimate in practical simulation, a new requirement would be presented and a new challenge would have to be faced.

The more we strove to match the exact feel of the airplane at different speeds and under different conditions of weight and of weather, the more deeply we became involved in the design and development of computers. The original Link Trainers used strictly mechanical means to move the trainer in response to an action in the cockpit and the degree of response was roughly the same each time a control was moved. In an airplane, if a pilot is flying at 100 mph and moves the stick slowly to the left and coordinates the turn with slight left rudder pressure, a banking turn results. The instruments show what is happening and the pilot feels he is turning. If again in an airplane the pilot moves the stick and rudder sharply to the left, the instruments move abruptly and he feels a strong G force indicating he is turning steeply. As the airplane speed increases to 200 or 300, or even 400 mph, the force of the turn is felt much more severely.

In our early trainers we were unable to simulate this variation in feel and instrument response since the combinations of springs and bellows and motors responded identically, regardless of the speed of the airplane or the abruptness with which the controls were moved. As we sought to refine the responses of our simulators, we recognized that every movement of the aircraft controls at any simulated speed should result in a precise and measurable response in the instruments and to the pilot. We also recognized that if we were to achieve consummate accuracy in our trainers, we were going to have to find a means of mathematically measuring what was happening in an infinite number of conditions ranging from what occurred when a pilot, for example, moved his controls gradually at low speed to abruptly at high speed. The instrument readout and feel would be constantly varying and would be affected by power application and whether the airplane was climbing or descending or, as indeed might be possible, the airplane was on its back.

Simply realizing that the forces affecting the airplane at any instant were precise and measurable was not the same as finding the constantly changing answer. If one could stop the airplane in mid-maneuver and calculate every force and effect in a fraction of a second and then introduce the information into the instruments in the cockpit while at the same time provide a realistic feel to the pilot, one would then come close to having a possible solution to the problem. The trouble would be, however, that in the next fraction of a second the conditions would inevitably change and all the calculation would have to be done again, and again in the next instant of time, so that, in effect, there is a continuous stream of complex calculations being performed with the results being delivered to the instruments and to the movement of the simulator. Of course, it's impossible for any human to perform such mathematical wizardry, but the miracle of a computer can.

Initially, we began to use the analog computers in this highly complex work in our simulators, and since no manufacturer produced such computers ready made, we had to design and build them ourselves. The simplest example of the analog computer is the speedometer in your car. It shows how much speed the car has and is therefore analagous to how fast the wheels are turning. Its drive mechanism is a simple cable connected to a device that measures the speed of the wheel, but it would be possible to measure this speed through electronic means. In a sense, this is what our computers do. They measure electronically what would happen with an airplane when it banks and turns and dives and climbs, and calculates the forces that would be on the controls. We can then introduce the exact force into our simulator so that the pilot feels as he would if he were actually flying and his instruments read as they would if he were actually performing a maneuver.

While analog computers allowed us to bring a much higher degree of accuracy to our simulators, they had shortcomings too. They could supply a mass of information quickly and with greater accuracy than we had ever been able to achieve before, but they were also relatively imprecise in that they could not produce exact information as could a computer that produced a finite quantity for every calculation. This quality was reserved for a further advance in the computer field with the development of the digital computer.

The simplest example of the digital computer is the odometer in a car. This registers in numbers the distance in miles the car has travelled. It is relatively precise, having in some cars measurement to tenths of a mile. It would be possible to construct an odometer that could measure distance to hundredths and thousandths and even smaller units of a mile, but as long as the result was displayed in units of measure, it would qualify as a digital computer. In our simulators the rapidity and accuracy with which it performs its mission makes it an essential part of achieving accurate simulation. For unlike the automobile's odometer, which is performing one simple function, we ask our computers to perform hundreds of different computations every instant and to provide accuracy to a high degree. Today, while Link is not generally considered as being in the computer business, we have designed and built for our own use more special purpose analog and digital computers than many companies whose main business is computers.

Our experience and skill in this highly technical field was surely a contributing factor in our winning, on May 29, 1952, a contract to develop a simulator for the six-engine B-47 bomber built by Boeing. This trainer was to have all the refinements of the F89D, including a few little extras such as a slight bump and lift at the instant of bomb-drop, and a period of extended float on landing, depending on landing weight.

Built with the electronic control console along one side of the trainer, and flanked by huge flight recording graphs, the trainer offered great flexibility in instruction. It could be used for long-range bombing missions, as well as for surveillance flights. The replica of the tandem cockpits of the B-47 Stratojet was complete in every detail and was termed by its students "too real for something that's buckled down."

Perhaps part of our success with the B-47 was due to our dogged determination to get information on performance and handling characteristics by actually flying in the airplane. Since the plane itself was being developed concurrently with the trainer, values and specifications were constantly changing, and, more importantly, civilians were not allowed in the plane at this stage of its development.

Finally, however, we were given permission to fly in the huge bomber and Dr. John M. Hunt, project manager for us, and I went to Wichita, Kansas, for the flight. I sat in the co-pilot's seat and Hunt in the observer's position in the nose. We took off, and flew around the Kansas sky for an hour or more, being hugely impressed with the great bomber, and at length we came in for landing. As it happened, the airspeed indicator was malfunctioning that day, so that as we dragged in on approach the airplane suddenly let go and landed hard in a cornfield short of the runway. It took a huge bounce and managed to dish down safely onto the runway. Later, with some embarrassment, Hunt told the pilot, Lt. Col. Pat Fleming, that from his vantage point in the observer's position he could see the famous test pilot's feet on the rudder pedals and he noticed that after the landing there was a pronounced shaking of the legs and feet on the pedals and he asked if that kind of vibration was a characteristic of the airplane during roll out after landing. "Hell no," replied Fleming, "I was shaking with fright."

The largest trainer ever built by the Link Company was the D-2 navigation simulator made in 1954. It was the first ever designed to provide for simulated polar flight. In a sense, the D-2 was a descendant of the first Link celestial navigation trainer (LCNT) built in 1941.

The D-2, however, was light years more complicated and advanced. The basic structure was a twenty-two-ton spherical house of tubular steel, which was set on two axles to permit it to move in any direction. More than five hundred tiny lights, accurately placed on the inside surface of the dome, duplicated the major stars of thirty-one constellations over the Northern Hemisphere and part of the Southern Hemisphere.

Student navigators, training in celestial navigation, stood on a rotating platform inside the dome. By shooting the stars with a sextant, they could get a "fix" and then plot their ground position. Speeds up to 1,750 mph and altitudes of 100,000 feet could be simulated in the trainer.

The huge device had facilities to train thirty students simultaneously. Six students could occupy star-sighting positions while twenty-four were plotting fixes and courses. The relationship between the instructor and the student navigator on a training mission was much the same as that between the pilot and navigator during an actual flight. The instructor flew the plane according to directions given him by the student navigator, and as the aircraft passed over the earth, the huge dome rotated to simulate the plane's motion. While the dome moved, a recorder in the instructor's area graphically plotted the ground route of the flight. By referring to the recorder after completion of the flight, the instructor could review ground position of the flight at any given moment.

The trainer's huge celestial dome, which had an inside diameter of thirty-seven feet, utilized a gear ratio of 120,000 to one, making it possible for a mere one-fiftieth horsepower motor—smaller than that used in a washing machine—to drive the multi-ton dome.

There was an ironic touch to our completion of the D-2 trainer, for a severe economy wave was in progress at the time and Congress had decreed that no new building could be constructed. Unhappily, the Air Force had no building large enough to house the huge trainer, so it was standing out of doors at an airport in California. With a little deception in its heart, the Air Force petitioned Congress for an "environmental sheath and temperature barrier" to complete the trainer. Congress wasn't fooled, however, and after some questioning the Air Force acknowledged this was indeed a functional description of a building. Fortunately, Congress approved the funds.

The D-2 navigation simulator was typical of the type of trainer Link and other manufacturers were turning out by the end of the Korean War. The day of the mass-produced, general-purpose flight trainer was passing, and complex, electro-mechanical computers were coming into use. These new trainers insured that each flight simulator's instrumentation performed the same as that found in aircraft cockpits. The cockpits in trainers became replicas of specific aircraft types. Control "feel"—again, by specific aircraft type—was duplicated with precision. Trainers came complete with the latest in simulated radio aids and navigation equipment. The instructor's station was equipped with automatic graphic flight recorders, duplicate cockpit instruments, and the controls required to create the kind of emergency flight conditions and mechanical malfunctions a pilot might actually encounter in the air.

As the speed and complexity of jet aircraft increased, so increased our efforts to meet training requirements. With the acceptance of the Convair F-102A Interceptor, the first delta-winged, all-weather interceptor to break the sound barrier, and the assignment of Link Aviation to produce the F-102A simulator, we had to stretch our know-how to meet the needs of this new kind of plane. The resultant equipment was the first simulator ever built in the United States incorporating a direct-current (D-C) computer system. It was also the first supersonic simulator built by our company. It featured a new and highly flexible linear interpolator system, making possible more precise computations over a greater range of variables.

From the student's standpoint, the outstanding advantage of D-C analog computation was the vast improvement in simulated flying qualities. Certain inherent shortcomings in alternating-current (A-C) computation arising from use of electro-mechanical integrators were overcome, providing more stable instrument indications, and more realistic flight characteristics. Furthermore, the flight characteristics of a d-c simulator are completely predictable during design.

With the advent of multi-mission military jet aircraft, came a change in procurement policy. No longer was reference made to aircraft alone, but to a complete weapon system. While Link had previously produced many training devices for use by the Navy, the A-5A built for North American Aviation, Inc., was the first complete weapon system trainer built by Link. It included both analog and digital computation, as well as complex visual and radar presentations.

The complexity of the A-5A trainer was reduced through use of a Link-developed, solid-state, digital function generator. This computer package was designed to be integrated into an analog computation system. Its inputs were the result of analog-to-digital conversion and its operation was the generation of functions of many variables by reference to a magnetic drum. The outputs, when converted to analog form, re-enter the analog computing system.

Even more complex than the A-5A trainer is the Link-produced F-4C weapon system trainer, the electronic and ground-based counterpart to the highly versatile McDonnell Douglas F-4C aircraft. This all-weather, two-man supersonic jet is designed for both high-altitude interception and long-range attack missions. Its avionic systems complement includes an inertial navigation and attack system, an all-altitude bombing computer, ground mapping and attack radar, and an armament computer for Sparrow and Sidewinder missiles. Not unlike our standard flight simulators, the F-4C weapon system trainer provides extremely accurate simulation of the aircraft's flight, engine and handling characteristics. In addition, it provides complete aircraft tactics simulation. This complex interrelation of flight controls, fire controls, navigation, bombing and automatic pilot enables crews in training to learn any and all characteristics of the offensive and defensive capabilities of the aircraft.

Still operating on the weapon system concept, we later designed and produced the B-58 bomber aircraft simulator, the first simulator of a supersonic bomber. The simulator was produced for the Air Force's Air Materiel Command under contract to Convair, the weapon system prime contractor and manufacturer of the B-58 Hustler.

In 1964 we were approached in a most unorthodox and devious way about building a very special simulator. We provided information on our capability and expressed interest in knowing more about the project. It turned out that we were being considered for the SR-71 simulator. This airplane is the fastest and probably the most sophisticated airplane in the world. It was designed by Kelly Johnson's outfit at Lockheed's famous Skunk Works.

We won the contract and plunged into the job of developing a simulator for the SR-71. A year later amid much secrecy, we delivered the device to the Air Force. It is still in operation. The SR-71 simulator was among the most sophisticated ever built. It had motion systems, plus simulation of all the on-board sensors that the airplane carries and, to my knowledge, was the first simulator for a multimach airplane.

The secrecy surrounding the SR-71 was somewhat eased when Lyndon Johnson became President. He was informed of the program and immediately disclosed it to the public. As a sidelight, it was originally called the RS-71, but in his announcement President Lyndon B. Johnson misread his notes, calling it the SR-71. That designation stuck.

After delivery of the SR-71 simulator, I received a letter from Kelly Johnson. It read: "Last Friday, October 15, 1965, the Air Force took delivery of the SR-71 simulator, which we jointly developed. Although we still have a number of open work items, I wanted to express my deep appreciation to your management and personnel for a job well done." I am proud of that letter.

Perhaps our experience with the SR-71 helped us win the contract to build a simulator for the F-111, the most advanced military aircraft then conceived. The simulators are designed to train both the aircraft commander and the second crewman, who is both copilot and systems operator.

The F-111 is the world's first operational aircraft with variable sweep wings. With wings extended straight out, the aircraft is capable of relatively short field performance. With wings swept part-way back, it cruises comfortably at less than the speed of sound for long distances. With wings swept fully back, it can fly over two-and-one-half times the speed of sound. Our task was to build a simulator that reproduced all of these conditions.

The plane also has what is probably the most advanced avionics systems of any aircraft. Its terrain-following radar automatically guides the craft as it flies at supersonic speed at altitudes below 500 feet, following the earth's contour up and down in tune with every earthly wrinkle.

The F-111's electronic subsystems supply data for automatic radar bombings. The attack radar system generates a picture of ground or airborne targets, regardless of visibility. At the same time, it calculates the changing range between the plane and target, corrects any navigational errors and performs radar photography. Aptly termed a weapons delivery system, the F-111 can carry a payload of nuclear or conventional weapons or a combination of both, over four times heavier than that of a World War II strategic bomber.

In another area, helicopters are constantly proving their worth in such diverse areas as commuter travel between congested metropolitan cities, performing rescue missions, and providing a vital communications link to inaccessible and remote areas. In military applications, the helicopter has truly come of age. Virtually every television newscast depicts the helicopter in a variety of roles including the rapid movement of troops to combat areas, the efficient support of ground actions, and the speedy removal of wounded to rear areas. The proven flexibility of the helicopter in both military and commercial applications continues to expand production of such aircraft. And more aircraft means more pilots— helicopter aviators—who must be trained in the operation of a highly sophisticated aircraft with unique aerodynamic characteristics, and capabilities not available to other type aircraft.

In 1954 we produced a two-seater helicopter trainer, which was adapted to the Bell H-13 military helicopter and trained pilots chiefly in operating helicopters under visual flight rules. The trainer was equipped with an electronically controlled Compensated Offset Projection System (COP). This was designed to make it appear a pilot was actually flying over terrain. The simulator could perform rolling and pitching movements up to inclinations of 13 degrees, as well as rotating movements through 360 degrees. The terrain simulated in the COP projector measures up to 250 square feet, depending upon the simulated height of the flight.

Our latest helicopter trainer design is called the Synthetic Flight Training System (SFTS), developed in cooperation with the U.S. Army. Although the SFTS is planned to simulate a specific aircraft, the basic design is such that with minor alterations to the cockpit configuration and the software package other helicopters within the same general classification can be simulated as well.

The Link SFTS is a generation in advance of simulators in current use by military and commercial aviation. It enables one instructor to train four helicopter pilots simultaneously through extensive application of computer controlled learning situations, an advanced motion system, and a comprehensive pilot measurement system for performance analysis.

Each of the four training stations duplicates the actual aircraft cockpit and includes a five-degree-of-freedom motion system, providing pitch, roll, heave, yaw and lateral translation. New design advances incorporated in the trainer also capture, in high fidelity, actual rotor aerodynamic characteristics. The resultant realism enables pilot trainees to experience all the motion cues of helicopter flight, including problems such as power failure, control malfunctions and the inevitable rough air. Aural cues such as engine and blade sounds are also included.

In addition, an electrical and mechanical fail-safe system provides for the safe return of the simulator to a level and locked horizontal position in the event of normal or emergency shutdown.

A sophisticated control station enables the instructor to automate virtually all the routine actions normally required of him. Freed from the need to manipulate controls and switches, the instructor is able to provide personal help and guidance to pilot trainees, while the automated system provides direction and an objective analysis of the pilot trainees' performance.

Prior to the students' arrival, the instructor conducts a morning readiness check by inserting a tape in the computer. He then inserts the appropriate computer and audio tape and assigns the trainees to their cockpits. Each of the four pilot trainees is then exposed to a different problem.

The pilot trainee begins each problem by listening to a standardized, tape-recorded briefing. This is followed by a demonstration during which the computer flies the simulated aircraft through the maneuver just as an experienced instructor would. Appropriate audio commentary on what to look for and to do at various times is keyed to the demonstration. Following the briefing and demonstration (which the trainee can repeat, if he wishes), the trainee flies the mission himself. During the flight the computer measures the trainee's performance and makes the lesson easier or more difficult according to the individual's progress. The level of difficulty is varied by modifying such factors as turbulence, malfunctions and communications load.

During the flight plots are made of ground track for both cross-country and approach modes, and records are kept on any aircraft parameters desired such as airspeed and altitude. Recording of air-ground communication is also made. These plots are used by the instructor for debriefings and critique. Records of trainee performance data, in a format suitable for magnetic tape recording, are available for research.

The Link SFTS simulators could also be used to train V/STOL (Vertical/Short Field Takeoff or Landing) pilots. V/STOL aircraft capabilities have matured considerably in the past few years due, in part, to experience gained in Vietnam. But as often happens, progress gained in military experience often is useful in commercial fields. It is expected that the fundamental capability of V/STOL aircraft will play an important role in terminal area support of the next generation of transport jets. We expect our SFTS trainers to play an important part in speeding V/STOL capability to the public.

The importance of flight trainers for the general aviation field has not escaped our notice in recent years. The market potential in this field is enormous and the opportunities great. The problems, it may be noted, are also substantial. While there are some 750,000 licensed pilots and 130,000 airplanes in the general aviation community and a doubling of these figures is projected in the next ten years, it is also true that the original training and recurrent training of these pilots is and will most likely continue to be in the hands of hundreds of schools and airport operators around the country. Most of these operators and the flight instructors they employ seem to prefer to have the instruction given in an airplane rather than a simulator or trainer. When trainers are used, darned if we don't find that the major competition for our new general aviation trainers is none other than the surplus military blue box Link Trainers, modified slightly and updated to make them usable as elementary instrument trainers.

The cost of these surplus units is minimal and it is a relatively easy task to reinstrument, repaint and rework these old C-8 and even C-11 trainers that the military has discarded and offer them as basic trainers in flight schools. And they are still useful and dependable, serving a worthwhile purpose in today's flight training programs. But the problem, from our standpoint, is that they never seem to wear out, and the spanking new general aviation simulators we now have on the market cost in the vicinity of $10,000. These new simulators do a great deal more than even the most extravagantly renovated and modernized blue box. The earliest of our GAT (General Aviation Trainer) flight trainers was produced in 1960, and did not have motion. It did include all of the basic flight instruments of general aviation aircraft and included a radio setup comparable to what might be found in well-equipped corporate-owned general aviation aircraft. A console and desk adjoining the trainer allowed an instructor to monitor the student's progress and to act as an air traffic controller in instrument flight problems.

While the original general aviation trainer, designated the Model 60, was moderately well received, it soon became clear that future trainers and simulators would need motion systems if they were to gain major acceptance with flight schools and with the FAA. And it seemed to us that if simulators were ever to achieve the position of importance in general aviation that they occupied with the airlines, the FAA would have to permit a substantial amount of a student's training hours to be taken in a simulator. Concurrently, a number of research projects were conducted to determine if new flight students could be taught to fly safely by taking the majority of their instruction in simulators and a small number of hours in an airplane, even though many studies had previously been conducted. The progress and achievement of the students was then compared with students taking all or most of their instruction in an airplane. The results were positive in favor of the simulator-trained students in every study ever conducted. The FAA then set out to determine if all general aviation simulators were of equal value and, if not, what standards should be established for simulators before they could be accepted as substitutes for actual flight time. This question is still being resolved.

Meanwhile the military was resolving a question that had plagued us and other simulator manufacturers since the time of the 1940's when the question of the need of motion was vigorously discussed at Link. We had originally used motion in the early trainers designed by Ed Link. Later, we moved from that concept largely at my insistence and in the face of violent disagreement from Ed. Still later we returned to highly sophisticated motion systems in both military and commercial airline simulators. But the question of whether or not motion trainers were inherently better than stationary trainers remained largely a matter of individual preference until the military conducted a variety of tests to find the answer. The results were unequivocally in favor of suitable motion systems in simulators. Even in the militarese of the final report, the point cannot be mistaken:

> a. A fixed-base cockpit should not be used to judge pilot performance or to judge the fitness of an individual to be a pilot.
> b. A moving-base cockpit, even for an instrument trainer, provides a substantial improvement in training realism.
> c. Sophisticated flight simulators should not be purchased by the United States Air Force without motion systems of comparable sophistication.

That conclusion, along with our own experience with motion, prompted us to design our current GAT 1 with a full motion system. More advanced general aviation trainers for twin-engine aircraft and for jet aircraft training are in the marketplace. Known as the GAT 2 and 3, respectively, they offer, we believe, the finest state-of-the-art simulators in general aviation today.

7

The Airlines and the Computer

Our success in building "sophisticated" military simulators prompted us to approach the airlines in the mid-'50's to see if we could interest them in our advanced training devices. Airlines had been using trainers since January 6, 1937, when American Airlines purchased a Link Model "C" to become the first airline to use a trainer. In the same year, United Airlines, Pan American, Australia National Airways, Eastern Airlines, and BOAC also bought pilot-makers to train their airline crews.

During and after the war, airlines used modified military trainers for refresher courses and in instrument approach practice. Pan American World Airways, for instance, kept five Link units busy most of the time, particularly in radio compass training.

Although many airlines were using basic trainers, none had ordered a specialized simulator designed for the aircraft they were flying. We first attempted to sell simulators for airplanes such as the DC-6 and the Boeing 377, but the airlines were undecided as to the best way of using these sophisticated and expensive devices. One airline wanted to try putting a DC-6 simulator in the back of a DC-3 or a DC-4 so that it could be ferried from base to base. Thus, the pilots could be trained without having to come to a central training location.

Another airline, while committed to the idea of a central training base for all crew members, balked at the idea of paying hundreds of thousands of dollars for a training device. Before the arrival of our electronic computerized simulators, the most expensive commercial trainer ever bought didn't exceed $20,000. Our new simulator could cost ten times that amount. Finally, one airline compromised by taking a cockpit or shell that they used in crew cockpit training and hired a small inexperienced company to build instruments and controls to resemble those in their aircraft. Of course this cost a fraction of what our simulator cost, but the training benefit was also a fraction of what could be achieved with a specialized simulator.

The first airline to place an order for a full simulator was Pan American, and I must report they bought it from Curtiss-Wright thanks much to the sales efforts of Ward Davis, who was originally trained by Karl Kail while Kail was a U.S. Air Force instructor in 1934. Curtiss went on to get most of the business for the DC-6 and DC-7 propeller-driven aircraft. We, having built the F-80A5 for the Air Force, were really much more experienced with jet aircraft simulators. Alan Williford decided, therefore, that our best strategy would be to drop out of competition in the propeller-driven commercial type simulator and concentrate on the jets, which we believed would be the airplane in the airlines' future. When the airlines did buy jet aircraft in the mid-50's, we were ready for them.

Meanwhile, we had to content ourselves with being the major supplier of general purpose trainers, such as the latest version of our C-8 or Model "F" types, and we sold a significant number of these to the airlines around the world.

As it became apparent that we could be in strong competition with Curtiss-Wright in the jet simulator field, Curtiss, in an effort to protect its position, sued us for infringement on a number of Dehmel patents involving a Convair-type trainer sold to Flight Safety, Inc. The suit dragged on for years during the middle '50's. Finally the judgment decreed that a number of the patents were invalid and that the few that were held to be valid, we had not infringed. Although we were held to be completely free, a great deal of time and a significant sum of money was needed to establish our position.

With the conclusion of this suit and with the introduction of the first commercial jet transport, we decided that our opportunity to break into the commercial field was here. Our first opportunity came as the Douglas Aircraft Company decided to buy a DC-8 jet simulator for research and training. We launched into a head-to-head competition with Curtiss for the Douglas order. We both wanted the business desperately since this would be one of the first units bought. Our offering was for a D-C analog device similar to what we'd built in our B-47 simulator. Curtiss was selling its earlier A-C analog model. We stressed to the Douglas engineers that our D-C device would be more suitable for research and more accurate for training, although it was more expensive than the competition. After an agonizing period of evaluation and analysis, we won the order making this the first time that two companies were producing simulators for the same aircraft. Here was an opportunity for a direct comparison of production capability as well as technical skill, for Curtiss was awarded a contract for a DC-8 from Pan American.

We, at Link, were first to deliver our commercial jet simulators in September, 1958, to United Airlines and Douglas. Two "rollouts" were held simultaneously, with the Douglas unveiling taking place at their company's new training center in Los Angeles. The United demonstration was held at the airline's big training center in Denver. The Link DC-8 simulator was the first simulator to be completed and "flown" prior to the first flight of the new aircraft.

When a crew entered the DC-8 simulator cockpit, it observed the exact replica of an actual aircraft cockpit. Operation requirements were exactly the same as in a real DC-8. Instruments and gages were checked as aboard the airplane, and radio contact was made with an airway traffic control center. Engine sounds were provided and controls responded to the various conditions of takeoff, climb and descent. Air speed, altitude, and fuel gages showed the relevant readings as the flight proceeded. While banking and turning, ascending and descending, the cockpit moved appropriately supported on hydraulic cylinders. From the control center, the radio operator would set up landing situations, varying from midday brightness to the darkness of night, with minimum outside visibility.

Behind the flight crew was a control panel known as the "trouble console." Here an instructor introduced flight emergencies. He would, for example, cause the instruments to indicate a malfunction of one or more of the engines. The pilot and crew would then have to respond to this emergency according to prescribed procedures. Many of the emergencies such as failure of two or more engines, or engine fire, could never be practiced in the airplane, yet gave a crew the opportunity to deal with these problems in a realistic environment. The DC-8 simulator training was so effective that captains from less complex aircraft could, after only fifteen hours of training in the simulator, gain enough experience to make a smooth transition to jets.

At that time, the DC-8 was the most complete and versatile simulator ever produced. The D-C computation had increased simulation capabilities over the old A-C system and had simplified maintenance and performance changes. Automatic amplifier checking had also been incorporated, enabling pre-flight checking of computation systems in a matter of minutes. An integral part of the electronic computer sections was the amplifier checking system, which spotted component failures and incipient failures, verified correct performance, and tested each amplifier against pre-established standards.

It had a more complex engine simulation than had ever been developed and it had a new approach to motion. The rotating pitch and bank motion of the earlier trainers lacked realism. In the DC-8 simulator we had developed a motion system that produced some actual G's. A set of hydraulic rams in the front moved the cockpit both in pitch and bank.

But the major innovation with our DC-8 simulator was the Link Visual System, Mark IV. Utilizing closed-circuit television, the Mark IV system provided a remarkably realistic visual presentation of an airport runway and surrounding terrain during simulated takeoffs and landings. In operation, a television camera scanned a model airport and approach area. The camera representing the pilot's eye during take-offs and landings was linked to the simulator computers to insure accurate positioning and movement at all times. This "training moviehouse" actually consisted of an exact replica of a selected airport, complete with instrument runway and taxi strips fixed vertically to the wall. Facing the airport model was a television camera capable of moving parallel and at right angles to the runway. Its focus was controlled (via a computer) by the pilot's stick movements, so that its field of vision corresponded to the image which the pilot might see during an approach. A projector mounted above the trainer cockpit flashed the picture taken by the TV camera on to a fifteen-foot wide screen ahead of the cockpit windows. The light intensity of the screen picture could be varied to simulate visibility deterioration. This visual realism, coupled with complete instrument simulation and an effective cockpit motion system provided the highest degree of total training ever incorporated in a flight simulator. When other purchasers of the DC-8 saw our simulator, acceptance was assured. In rapid succession we received orders from SAS, KLM, Western, Japan, Trans-Canada, and Alitalia Airlines. There was no question in airline circles that Link had won the battle of DC-8 simulators.

Our success here led to contracts to build Boeing 707, Convair 880, and Lockheed Electra simulators. Among the customers for these trainers were TWA, BOAC, Qantas, National, Delta and, of course, our first airline jet simulator customer, United. With the flood of orders came a mountain of problems. As it happened, many of the aircraft for which we had simulator orders hadn't been built. They were on the drawing board, but not on the flight line. True, once the airplane is designed, the simulator can go forward, but variations also seem to emerge as the airplane flies.

In the Electra simulator, for example, our first unit was ordered by Eastern. They were extremely anxious to take delivery, but we were having problems. We had the trainer in flight test, but just couldn't make the simulator match the airplane characteristics as they were reported by one of their pilots. We finally found that during the first flights of the actual airplane there had been a problem with stability. Without our learning of it, a fix was made by adding to the horizontal stabilizer. After test flying the modified airplane, it was clear the stability problem was solved, but nobody thought to tell us. Our simulator continued to have the responses of the unmodified airplane. We had heated arguments about whether or not the simulator flew as it should. We kept pointing to the data supplied us. The pilot kept telling us he didn't care what the data said, it wasn't the same. Finally, someone thought to point out that the airplane had been modified and the correct data had not been supplied to us. We adjusted the simulator to conform to the new data, and all was well.

We took a beating in the early days of commercial simulators before we learned to beware of signing contracts with different airlines for supposedly the same airplane. Often the simulator turned out to be quite different because the airlines would specify entirely different interior equipment. One of the simulators we had contracted to build was for the Convair 880. We had contracts with TWA and Delta. We had based our price on the assumption both would be very much the same. It turned out that each had a different auto-pilot and, to make matters worse, neither of these had been fully developed. These problems caused serious delays in the development of some of our simulators and precipitated some financial woes. We survived, however, and braced ourselves for the competition from newcomers who were being attracted to the field. Redifon of England and CAE were two strong new companies. Curtiss was phasing out of the simulator business. Currently the heaviest competition for the airline-type simulators is the new wide-bodied jets. Another new entry, Conductron, won the DC-10 training and development order placed by Douglas. Other DC-10 simulators were ordered by American and United from Redifon. We were a strong competitor at American, but we lost that and won the contract for National Airline's DC-10 simulator. We also are the leaders in 747 simulators. Our first one was delivered to TWA in mid-1969.

One thing we quickly learned in trying to sell simulators to the airlines was that there had to be a strong economic benefit shown before an order would be obtained. We had to demonstrate that simulators make it easier to attain and retain higher levels of pilot skill than was possible in training in aircraft. We were able to do this by testing pilots trained in simulators and comparing the results with the aircraft-trained people. It soon became clear, moreover, that we had a strong case for persuading the FAA to substitute required flying hours for time in a suitable simulator. Reluctantly at first, but more willingly with the mounting evidence, this was done. The justification of the simulator became more qualitative than quantitative with the passage of time, for we could produce better pilots in less time at lower expense than was possible in aircraft training alone. Allan Bonnalie, who was the Director of Training and Simulation for United Airlines, and the staff at TWA probably had as much to do with the acceptance by the FAA of substitution standards of ground time for air time.

The use of flight simulation by the world's airlines has come a long way, but progress hasn't always been easy. Research and development costs have been high and in the early days pilot resistance to simulators was a factor to be considered. Captain E. P. Rordam, Eastern Airline's Director of Operations Training, recalls, "Most airline pilots at that time had accumulated several thousand hours and fifteen or twenty years of flying experience. An attitude and reaction to suggested changes had developed that was hard to dispute. I can't think of any group that is more suspicious of, and resistant to, change than airline pilots. This attitude was: 'I've survived over 3,000,000 miles of flying and coped with all the normal and abnormal situations that occurred. I must be pretty good or I wouldn't be here.' "

Although at first an ego deflator, the simulator rapidly became a confidence builder. Captain Rordam recalls: "It was accepted by the pilot group as a valuable training aid much sooner than we expected, largely because of experience gained on a particular maneuver—an 'engine fire' immediately after takeoff."

In such circumstances the natural tendency had been for all the crew to drop everything (sometimes including the plane) to combat the blaze. The simulator was programmed to instruct the captain to command the others to fight the fire so he could concentrate on his primary responsibility of flying the aircraft. This new training procedure worked so well that it was approved by the FAA.

Later, Captain Rordam reports, "The value of this type

of training was proved when one of our captains was confronted with the same situation in real life. He calmly gave the command, 'fight the fire,' and proceeded to do a beautiful job of flying back to the airport for a safe landing while one engine burned away."

As a result of this experience, trainees' attitudes changed. The captain says, "Most of those receiving simulator training recognized their increased level of proficiency after having had an opportunity to practice under the realistic conditions made possible by the simulator. Top management became sold on the concept of better trained crews and the possibility of decreasing aircraft training time, and consequently cost, by an approved simulator program.

"In one year at Eastern, we trained and promoted more than 1,500 flight crew members. Without our simulators it would have been physically impossible to qualify more than one-third of them. Today there just isn't enough time, air space, airports or aircraft to do the job without these ground-based machines."

Most airlines recognize today that they face severe economic penalties if the aircraft remains a primary means of transition training. The Air Bus (L-1011) at approximately $17 million and the SST at $37.5 million will present hourly operating costs that stagger the imagination. This fact will force minimum non-revenue aircraft flight training. A look at the past will give us some valuable hints as to what simulation can do for us in the future.

I remember asking an airline official at a training seminar, "How does the cost of simulator training compare to actual aircraft training?" He quickly replied, "We can train in the simulator for about one-third or less of what it would cost in the aircraft. That means we can do three times the training in a simulator and get twice the efficiency that we would in the aircraft."

Another director of flight operations added, "It's not only good economics, it's good operating procedure. We need the aircraft to serve our passengers and by strengthening our ground training, we increase the availability of our fleet for public service and for revenues. Because we have full control of the environment and operating conditions in the simulator, pilot training is often more effective on the ground than in the air."

Captain C. M. (Red) Stubben, Continental Airline's vice president of flight operations said, "Until we acquired our simulators, Continental did most of its training at night. Actually, of the first 1,000 hours that I flew during training, 800 hours were accumulated at night. And most of that was flown between one and four in the morning."

Captain Stubben continued, "Once I flew to Denver with a pilot who had just finished his training. His landing wasn't the best I had ever seen and when I commented on it said, 'You know, Red, this is the first landing I have made in the daytime.' He had gone through all of his training—the FAA proficiency check, everything—at night."

If we are to meet the training requirements of the future and survive the economic penalties associated with them, we must set our goal at nothing less than the capability of one hundred per cent simulation. We must be able to accomplish all aircraft training maneuvers with a fidelity of reproduction equal to the aircraft. When we reach this level, all training, as well as the rating ride, may be given in the simulator. The airline pilot of the future will go directly from the simulator to a revenue flight for his enroute training and final line check. This was the philosophy Captain Odagari of Japan Air Lines related to me in June 1970. But this day will not arrive until simulators are refined and improved even further.

There is still much that we don't understand about how a person flies an airplane. I often have engineers ask how I, who am not an engineer, am so certain about the characteristics of a particular airplane. The answer often is that I have flown that airplane. Most pilots know their airplanes well. The truth is that pilots still fly by the seat of their pants to some extent. Even with the most sophisticated instrumentation in the cockpit, they still feel what's happening. Out of the corner of their eye, they can detect movement and they tend to respond automatically. I used to fly a PT-17 and could look out and see without any artificial horizon if my wings were perfectly level.

The trouble with a simulator is that it is not an airplane. I can build the most sophisticated motion system possible and have it do exactly what the equations and all the data tell me to do, but the pilot may have reservations. There is always a missing element. We might call it the airplane personality. This intangible quality we can't build into a simulator, and it shows. Unfortunately all the formulae and equations can't quite capture the essence of an airplane. We know we will always be trying to improve our fidelity, but we know, too, that the essential difference between an airplane and a simulator will always exist.

In visual displays, too, we know there are serious shortcomings to what we would wish for. We have been

134

producing various types of visual display systems since 1942, and we are still striving for a better way to present a realistic panorama. Because of the urgent need for a technological breakthrough in this area, the use of lavish computational power to solve this problem must be given early consideration. Although the transition from analog to digital computation has improved existing visual systems, we are still a long way from using computer capability to the utmost. An entirely new approach to visual simulation is possible if extremely rapid computation can be obtained at reasonable cost. Consideration is being given to an automatic drafting-type machine that would employ one or more cathode ray tube projectors to generate line drawings similar to those prepared by draftsmen. Scenes, such as runways and hangars would be described by straightforward mathematics and drawn geometrically.

Good as our visual systems are, they still lack adequate illumination, adequate resolution and adequate field of view. Basically this seems to be caused by the fact that the human eye is a most wondrous organ. Our simulation systems are not able simultaneously to provide realistic enough resolution, illumination, field of view, and perspective to give a proper illusion of the real world. This becomes particularly evident when one considers the total visual problem associated with flying in a flight problem ranging from engine start, to takeoff, to altitude, through maneuvers, to landing pattern, to touchdown, and to the ramp.

We have tried on many occasions a variety of moving picture techniques, but the trouble is that the perspective of the picture is frozen at the moment you open the shutter of the camera. With the perfect visual system in a simulator, the pilot would do whatever he would normally do and the visual would show him what he would normally see as a result. If he turns right, the visual system should show him in a right turn. In movies, if the picture was programmed to show a left turn and the student made an error and turned right, the picture he would see would still be to the left. Obviously this would be confusing and unrealistic.

In an effort to solve some of these problems, we finally developed and delivered to Delta Air Lines a visual system called VAMP. This stands for Variable Anamorphic Motion Picture, and the system includes a series of different lenses, which afford an apparent perspective change over limited angular view when one looks at the picture. Actually, VAMP equipment uses TODD-AO, full-color, widescreen, 70 mm. motion pictures of real aircraft landings, takeoffs and approaches at any desired landing field. It wraps these scenes around the windshields. Fog or mist are simulated through special filtering techniques. The motion picture combined with servo-controlled distortion lenses and mirrors, enables what the trainee sees to be altered, depending on what the trainee is doing, to provide realistic simulation of variations from the ideal takeoff or landing. To date VAMP has been the most successful for the presentation of straight-in approaches and straight takeoffs and has been accepted for landing and takeoff training requirement for airline crew members by the FAA.

The first VAMP films were photographed from a helicopter at Chicago's O'Hare International Airport. Despite the heavy air traffic at the nation's busiest airport, the Link project was given top priority, sometimes at the expense of regular flight schedules. The undertaking would have been impossible without the wholehearted cooperation of the airport manager, controllers, Air Line Pilots' Association, CAB and local authorities. All of them realized that the project would benefit the entire aircraft and airline industry.

In contrast, when Hollywood filmed *Airport* based on Arthur Haley's book featuring O'Hare, a smaller airport had to be used because the actual locale was "too busy." Swallowing his pride, the director not only hired the Link pilot following completion of the VAMP project but also offered to buy some of the Link film for inclusion in his production.

Before the helicopter method of photography was chosen, two other ways were considered. One, of course, was using actual aircraft, but this was quickly ruled out because rental and camera installation costs would be prohibitive. Another possibility was using a light plane for air scenes and a truck with extended camera boom for taxiing shots. Experiments showed, however, that the boom was too bouncy.

The problem was complicated by the fact that each scene had to be shot at three different levels, corresponding to cockpit heights of various types of aircraft: *e.g.,* 20 feet for 737's, 30 feet for 707's and 60 feet for 747's. When a 747 landing scene was photographed for instance, the copter would descend to 60 feet above the touchdown point and then level off and "taxi" at that altitude above the runway and exit ramp. When finally the copter landed it did so on a specially-constructed "nest"—an enclosure made with railroad ties to protect the underslung camera. An airline official said, "It was worse than teaching your wife to drive into the garage."

Flying with such precision was a nerve-wracking job—so much so, in fact, that one pilot grounded himself in mid-project, suffering from nervous exhaustion. His successor, however, withstood the strain, having just returned from duty in Viet Nam.

Maneuvering the copter wasn't the only problem. Far from it! The 13-man crew had to overcome numerous technical hurdles. For example, the copter of course couldn't fly as fast as the aircraft which it was simulating so when the film is projected it has to be speeded up. For sequences showing highway traffic in the background, police were detailed to hold cars to a crawl so that when the film was accelerated the vehicles wouldn't zip by like animated cartoon creations. VAMP film is projected through four feet of glass. This could cause color distortion so a special type of glass had to be imported from Germany.

Weather was a matter of ceaseless concern. Rain and wind frequently delayed shooting schedules and the crew, during its six-week stint, often worked virtually around the clock to make up for lost time.

After the shooting it was learned that some of the film had the "shakes." When the prints were made, offsetting jitters were introduced to smooth out the final product. In some night scenes the flare from the strobe lights lining the runways was unrealistic. This was remedied by retouching 400 feet of film, frame by frame. Such corrective measures are costly but less expensive than reassembling the crew and reshooting. The result of this all-out effort is a flight simulation visual system of unsurpassed realism which one airline has hailed as fantastic.

VAMP is not the final solution to the visual problem. Its shortcoming is that it still offers only a very limited angular excursion envelope so that when one is three or four miles out on the glide path and localizer, one gets a realistic view only if one stays in a very narrow path left or right. As one gets in close, however, the linear distance circumscribed by the angle is so small that it is all but impossible to miss the runway. The problem is that it's almost impossible to pre-record all the possibilities since one can't predict all the variables.

TWA and the Dalto company are in the process of developing a multi TV camera probe, large model system, which will provide non-programmed viewing to both pilot and co-pilot, through forward wind screens and side windows. At this point it is too early to comment on the nature of resolution and illumination problems that will be encountered. Progress in visual systems will be made, but it will, I fear, be slow. On the other hand, progress in the development of the totally electronic fully computerized simulator has been rapid and its momentum will surely be sustained.

In the fall of 1960 solid-state digital computers started to come into their own. Prior to that time, they were expensive, comparatively slow and too cumbersome to be completely practical. It now looked feasible to develop a digital computer to really do the simulation job. In fact, modern digital computer technology permits a very close approximation of a real situation. But achieving this "real" situation also requires a "record" which is made possible by combining designer ingenuity with a data package that truly reflects the relevant performance of the aircraft to be simulated.

The importance of letting the nature of the problem to be solved govern computer choice was discussed in the June 1969 issue of *Space Aeronautics*:

Because of their high accuracy, exact repeatability and the wide variety of mathematical functions they can solve, digital computers should be used wherever possible. In a digital computer, accuracy of the order of 10 digits is not uncommon and repeatability is exact. In analog equipment 1 percent of full scale is considered good, an accuracy that seldom gives meaningful numbers beyond four digits (depending, of course, on scaling), and repeatability is nonexistent—a slight change in the amplifier or potentiometer setting results in a different answer. Nevertheless, problem requirements should dictate computer choice, a fact often overlooked by engineers who want the most sophisticated equipment regardless of problem requirements.

At the beginning, however, computer choice was largely a function of availability. Once, only analog computers were available for use in simulators; these produced continuous solutions, but lacked accuracy (no better than 0.1 percent) and repeatability. Greater accuracy (.01 to .001 percent) and good repeatability could have been achieved with digital computers, but they were very slow and in place of continuous solutions produced only sample data or periodic solutions. Until their speed was increased, this drawback made them unsuitable for the many problems requiring real-time solutions with either man or real system hardware in the loop.

The hybrid computer complex was introduced to take advantage of the unique capabilities of each of these systems—the analog for solving high frequency dynamics and digital for low frequency dynamics. Since the rotational high frequency terms and translational low frequency terms of vehicle dynamics can always be separated, the computer selected can always be matched to the required solution rate.

Flight behavior of the aircraft is described by aerodynamic coefficients and weight and balance data supplied by the airframe manufacturer in the form of performance curves, tabulations, and mathematical expressions. This data must be interpreted and reworked into a mathematical model. This resulting mathematical model can now be turned over to computer programmers for translation into computer language. The programmer is the bridge between the computer and the flight problem which is to be solved many times per second. He must be thoroughly familiar with both the capabilities of the particular computer to be used and the interactions of all elements of the problem itself. It is his job to prepare a list of detailed instructions that the computer can use to solve the flight problem.

Digital computers can obey a number of basic instructions but they are not mechanized to perform these instructions in any particular sequence. Therefore, the programmer must additionally structure the instruction sequence in order to provide solutions to the problem on the basis of real-time requirements. In a similar manner, many other programs are written for correct simulation of all "on-board systems" which include: fuel quantity; transfer gages and controls; hydraulic pumps, associated valves and pressure gages; radio receivers and their associated navigation instruments, flight path computers, and auto-pilot couplers. However, correct systems operation is not enough. There must also be simulated failures. During simulator design, highly experienced personnel from the using airline analyze all systems for typical failures and characteristic indications of these malfunctions. Having received the airline's requirements for simulated failures, the programmer inserts these failure "options" into the operational programs in such a way that they occur in a realistic manner. Simulation of system malfunctions is truly important because corrective actions to many failures can be taught safely only in a simulated environment. Extensive simulator tests are then conducted in conjunction with the airline experts to ensure that small dynamic indications, not present in or decipherable from the original data, are included. These transient indications are important clues to the using pilots and flight engineers, showing the true nature of how the various aircraft systems affect one another when operating together.

After doing some studies, we proposed a new generation of digital simulator for the new three-engine 727 airplane that was about to be delivered to Eastern and United. With the valuable leadership of Dr. John M. Hunt, Technical Director at Link, and Bill Wood we offered to develop a special purpose digital computer for this simulator. It was to be called the Mark I, and would consist of three parts. First was the main frame or central processor, to do the general arithmetical functions, integrations and the like, all of which had been worked out on paper. The second part was a function generator which could handle as many functions as necessary. And the third part was a DDP (Digital Data Preselector). In this was stored all the radio station information, as well as the data necessary for navigation problems. In the old analog equipment we could only handle up to twelve radio stations. These had to be laboriously set up by hand with the location and frequency cranked in. We now can provide information on between 500 and 1,000 stations, all fully stored and available for use at any time. These are fully automatic and extremely accurate.

After we made our presentation for this new kind of simulator, we held our breath, for this would be a breakthrough if we won the orders. At last we got the answer from both United and Eastern. Both said yes. So, we signed up the first two solid state digital computer simulators and then the hard work of actually developing and building them got under way. We began work on the Mark I with the idea that it should be economically justifiable for use under the existing cost structure, and should capitalize on the undeniable advantages of digital computation: high accuracy, extreme flexibility, high reliability, small size, and reduced heat dissipation.

The Mark I was a resounding success, and having learned the techique for building it, and with other technological advances, we then went on to build a Mark II. This was essentially the same as the Mark I except that all operating speeds were doubled. Then we jumped to the Link-built GP-4 computer, which was first incorporated into a DC-9 simulator. Its computing logic has the speed and capability to simulate two different aircraft simultaneously.

The GP-4 is slightly smaller than the Mark I, but it is three times faster and contains more than twice the memory capacity. The key to its great speed and small size is that its computing logic consists of aspirin-sized integrated microcircuits—the first used in large-scale scientific computers. An integrated circuit contains all its elements in an area smaller than that of a conventional solid-state transistor.

143

The GP-4 differs from most data processing computers in that it is designed for scientific use rather than for service application. It operates the simulator in real time—that is, it enables the simulator to respond to the pilot's maneuvers in the same time the airplane would. Considering that a jet flies ten miles per minute, the real-time simulation afforded by the GP-4 is imperative to provide real aircraft semblance. This remarkable device calculates every flight characteristic as many as twenty times per second.

The computer uses a magnetic drum memory to store programs and a magnetic core memory to store data. With this split-memory capability, the computer reads and executes instructions and extracts data simultaneously, thus increasing operating speeds. It executes nearly one-half million mathematical calculations per second.

Although it was primarily designed for use in flight simulators, the GP-4 has other potential uses, such as research and development simulation. In this role, the GP-4 would perform as it does with an actual airplane simulator, except that the simulated airplane would exist only on the drawing board and in the computer's memory bank. In the process control field, the GP-4 could be applied to large industrial plants.

One of Link's most important economic and technical contributions to simulation is the application of one GP-4 to operate singly or simultaneously two different simulators—a DC-8 and a DC-9, for instance. The computer's speed, capacity and advanced electronic design enable each crew to fly an independent training mission. For example, one crew of Mohawk Airlines, one of the first purchasers of the GP-4, can land at Syracuse Airport, while the other is taking off at

Kennedy International Airport. If the simulators are flown in the same area, the crews can communicate with each other just as they would in actual flight.

Motion systems are another area in flight simulation that require constant attention. Of course, motion cue generation has been an important part of flight training since the early Link Trainers first incorporated a bellows-type motion system. Over the years, Link has developed several highly effective motion systems of various degrees of complexity to meet different vehicle or operator requirements. The simplest type was the stick shaker system in which a buffer signal was fed into the control loading system to give the pilot a realistic stall buffet effect. The next type, known as a seat shaker was normally used when the cockpit itself did not include motion. More sophisticated cockpit motion systems which have been developed by Link in recent years include the cradle system, the two-point system and the three-point system. The three-point motion system, which was originally designed for the B-58 Flight Simulator and was incorporated in C-130 and C-135 simulators, was selected by NASA as the basic motion system to be used in facilities for research in supersonic transport simulation.

Our latest motion system, used in the Link 747 flight simulator, is the six-degree-of-freedom motion system. It is by far the most important contribution to the state-of-the-art of motion systems that has been made to date. Called the "flying cockpit system," it is a departure from the design of previous motion systems and provides pitch, roll and yaw motion as well as lateral, longitudinal and vertical movement—in six independent degrees of freedom. The design is based on a triangular bipod actuator arrangement that provides

145

high fidelity response characteristics with inherent stability. The hydraulic system that drives the actuators has the capacity to provide pilots both positional and acceleration cues while supporting a full-size 747 cockpit, instructor station, and visual system, weighing about ten tons.

Let's take a ride in the 747 simulator and see how it goes.

Approaching the huge simulator one is first struck with its enormous size and the complex of legs it rides on. A stairway and catwalk provide entrance to the spacious cabin area and there spread out in front of you is the array of instruments, switches, levers and dials that are the guts of the modern airplane. We pass the engineer's console, and since we're acting as pilot in command, we take the left-hand seat in the cockpit. Our copilot is at our right. We've been briefed beforehand on our flight so we know what our payload is and the fuel quantity we carry. Behind us at a separate console is the instructor, and a check pilot may ride a jumpseat between the two pilots' seats.

This is a night flight so the cabin is dark. So are the windows except for faint lights representing taxis and runway lights. As we switch on power, the hundreds of dials and instruments glow softly. Our maps and charts are ready as the co-pilot starts the checklist. We touch or point to every indicator he calls out, or we verify that the switch or control is in its proper position. Pages of the checklist go by before we are ready to start the huge engines. The toggle switches that activate the flow of fuel and fire the igniters are flipped and a distant whine builds to a muffled roar as number one engine sparks up to speed. As it comes to life, needles flicker and spin up to yellow. Red marks on the power dials then quietly stabilize. The process is repeated for the four engines. We're in radio contact with our operation people on the ramp and receive an OK to proceed with our flight.

A call to receive our Instrument Flight Rules clearance is taken and read back, and at last we call ground control for approval to taxi. We are ready to go. We release the brakes and advance power slightly. The simulator shudders and the lights we have been watching out a cockpit window slowly begin to slip by as we taxi. The simulator is rocking gently now as the irregularity of the ramp tilts it. We are sitting almost forty feet above the ramp and we must follow a precise path to our takeoff point. Directions come from ground control and we acknowledge them. The takeoff checklists occupy us now and soon we are ready. A last few items must be checked—controls free, all instruments scanned once more— and we line up ready to go. Ahead of us stretches two almost endless rows of lights converging 12,000 feet down the runway.

We call for power and gradually advance the levers that feed the giant engines. Slowly at first, then ever faster the lights race by us. The "plane" is pounding down the runway as the copilot calls out the critical phases of our takeoff. To test the simulator realism, and just for the fun of it, we press the left rudder very slightly. The simulator appears to move left as the rectangles of cement we have been watching slip beneath us veer to the right as the lights on our left come closer. We notice the check pilot tense slightly and then relax as we tap right rudder to bring us back to the center of the runway.

We've been racing down the runway for almost a full minute now and the end of that row of lights, which are now a blur on either side of us, is visible. The engine sound is clear and strong as we pass the point where we could safely slam the power levers into reverse and brake hard to bring the plane to a stop if something should go wrong. It's all go now as we glance at the airspeed indicator and see it creeping up to the point where we can safely rotate the nose and lift off. We scan the panel and see the needles that seem to be straining against their stops. The simulator is jiggling and bouncing now as it hits irregularities in the runway. Finally the copilot calls "rotate" as we glance at the airspeed to make sure that lift-off speed is there. It is and we pull back strongly though smoothly on the massive yoke.

Instantly there is a feeling of being lifted into the air as the sound of wheels on runway stops and the lights beside the runway disappear beneath us. We're safely airborne.

We call out a series of swift sharp commands and the co-pilot raises gear, then flaps. A deep thud and then a cluster of lights confirm gear is up, a soft whine far behind us and a receding needle show flaps are in place. Power levers are adjusted as we bring the airplane to its climb attitude. We're strictly IFR (Instrument Flight Rules) now and the cockpit windows show only a ghostly blank. We've stabilized the airspeed now and we're watching the proper instant to start our noise abatement turn. Here it is and we bank gently holding airspeed and watching for signs of trouble. We could lose an engine anytime now. We've been through this in our minds a hundred times, but there is nothing like doing it to know you know it.

All quiet. We're climbing away on course, talking with departure control, and are settling down for a climb to altitude. This could run twenty minutes. But don't relax yet, something could happen any second. Still nothing. We're going through 18,000 feet. All's well. Then there it is. Just a flicker of the fuel pressure indicator, but then it's back to normal and nothing happens. We sit ready to pounce on any problem. Still nothing. We relax a bit. Maybe we could risk a cigarette. Better not, not yet anyway.

Oops here it comes. That fuel pressure indicator sinks to zero and a change in engine sound indicates a flame-out. Sharply we call it to the copilot and give the orders for checklist and contact the field for an emergency return and landing. As he makes the call, I'm searching for the reason for the failure. Is an air start possible? We try and it's no good. We've done the announcement to the passengers and we've got to jettison fuel and work our way down for a landing. The inoperative engine is shut down and things have quieted a bit when a dull explosion racks the left side of the airplane. The 747 lurches wildly as needles unwind crazily. It's hard to remember we're in a simulator now as all our experience tells us to look for the trouble and correct it if possible.

We're barking orders to the copilot now and have gripped the yoke with one hand as we grip the power levers with the other. We're under control, but tension is high. It's almost certain one of the turbine blades in the engine has torn loose and torn up the wing. It might have ruptured fuel cells and electrical lines, so we must isolate the damaged area as quickly and effectively as possible. We've reported our situation and started down. Two engines are out, both on one side and the huge airplane is slanting through the sky as the power on the two remaining engines tries to force us to fly in a wide circle while the controls fight to counteract this. The two dead engines are secured and we're receiving headings from the ground to position us for approach. Radios are tuned for an instrument approach as we let down. Checklists again. What have we forgotten? Everything seems in order as the needles on the panel tell us we're close to the field and on a proper glide path. Suddenly the runway lights appear through the window and we reduce power, watch the airspeed, check gear and flaps. There's an airplane landing far ahead of us. He will have turned off by the time we want to land. Easy now. Suddenly the airplane on the runway gives a sickening lurch and slides across the runway. Its gear has collapsed. He is blocking the runway—we have got to go around. Damn. Quickly now. Gear up, full power, raise the nose slightly. Establish a gradual climb, checklist again. We're sweating and swearing at the same time. The tower calls and we've got to use a different runway. That means different approach procedures. The copilot is readying the radios and handling communications.

The check pilot sits quietly between us.

At last we're lined up again, and we sail over the threshhold of the runway with speed on the button and wait for a little sink onto the concrete. There's a gratifying squeak and bump as the wheels touch. We taxi back working the checklists again as we shut down. We slump limply in the seat as the check pilot says, "Good flight." The door opens onto a brightly lighted hangar and we walk shakily down the steps, eyeing the grotesque angled legs of the simulator. These are the hydraulic plungers that heave the five tons of simulator around to provide the feeling of liftoff and motion of flight.

This, then, is the 747 simulator. It is one of the largest aircraft simulators ever built, and it offers the most realistic visual and motion systems ever produced. It can train a pi-

lot and crew to a high point of proficiency, and if used im-
properly, it can reduce an experienced pilot to a sweating,
frustrated and resentful man. For the problems that can
be introduced are so varied and so realistic that a pilot can
be brought to a point where he may throw up his hands and
quit. This brings up a matter that both we and the users of
our equipment are constantly studying. This involves the
proper role of the instructor. In general, we feel that the
best results are obtained from simulators when the frequency and seriousness of the problems thrown at a pilot are
kept to reasonable limits. Most airlines plan their proficiency
training with this in mind. But there are still a few tough
situations which, although their incidence in actual flight is
very low, could happen and must be practiced. The two engines out on one side is such a problem and should not be
practiced in an airplane where mistakes or lack of proficiency
cannot be tolerated.

With motion systems becoming larger, fidelity becoming
greater and the realism of visual attachments improving, we
can depend more and more on the simulator for our training. But here we must also analyze our training techniques.
In the old days, pilots infrequently spent time in the blue
box. Today they accept it as an important and necessary part
of their training program. In the years to come we are confident new approaches will become more acceptable in advanced training. Although we know pilots don't like it, there
will be automatic checking and scoring built into simulators.
As the new breed of pilots comes along, they will realize this
is important.

The time will surely come when as a pilot flies a simulator
mission, the instant he does something wrong, the instructor

can hit a stop button and run an instant replay. A tape will back up as it does on TV during a football game. The instructor will say, "Now, hands off, Captain. We are going to let the simulator, which just recorded your last thirty seconds of flight, show you what you did. You just watch your instruments as we now duplicate what you did." After another run through, the instructor can point out improvements and say, "That time you did a lot better."

The pilot may not like it, but eventually such records will become part of his permanent record.

We are now putting displays in some of our 747 and 1011 simulators that allow the instructor to read airspeeds and attitude deviations with great accuracy. During a simulated approach the instructor can push a button and have a permanent record made of how far off the desired airspeed the approach was. This kind of procedure is terribly demanding, but it is necessary if we are to have fully competent pilots at the controls of our SST's and the new generation of airplanes.

8
Simulation and the Space Program

Our first involvement with the space program came about as a result of our strong suspicion that simulators were going to prove to be vital to the success of space exploration. We had made the decision some years before to investigate fields other than aviation as possible areas to apply our simulation knowledge. When we learned that the Department of Defense was interested in a study of space needs, and was encouraging us to bid on the project, we jumped at the chance to become involved. A major problem quickly emerged however, for we soon learned that the Department of the Air Force wished to pay for these studies at the rate of one dollar regardless of how much the participants expended. The military felt with some justification that the opportunity for learning was so great, and the consequent likelihood of those participating in getting contracts later, that they felt the token payment of one dollar was ample reward.

While their thinking was encouraging, there still remained the matter of convincing management of the desirability of investing heavily in an area where a return might be years away if indeed there was a return at all. Dave Mason was

President of Link at the time, and it fell to me to explain the situation to him. I opened by reporting that we had a request to bid in a new field of simulation, and that our involvement could run well up over a quarter of a million dollars. He agreed that this was fine until I told him our remuneration was to be the sum of one buck. He turned kind of pale and somewhat testily suggested that the President's office was a lousy place for jokes of that sort. I told him that this was no joke and that in spite of the risk, this seemed like a great opportunity to get into an area that would challenge our skills to the utmost, and at the same time offer us a reasonable chance for a return on our investment in the future. After some discussion with members of our engineering team, he agreed that we should get involved, and in short order we were knee deep in space.

After the original study contract, we worked on a variety of projects, but the first time we completed a full simulator was in 1964 when we delivered the T-27 space flight simulator which is now based at the Aerospace Research Pilot School at Edwards Air Force Base. The project started out as a simulator for the X-20 Dinosaur, a controllable short winged glider that could be launched from a high flying airplane. It was thought at one time that this might provide a means of returning astronauts to earth after space flights. The simulator also was to be used as a general purpose trainer for Air Force research and the indoctrination of space pilots. Unfortunately, the simulator was not finished until after the X-20 project was cancelled, and thus it became a kind of basic trainer for prospective astronauts. It served very well in that capacity due in part to the aid and advice of Colonel Chuck Yeager, who had participated in many of the early fixed-wing airplane rocket powered flights to the edge of space.

The trainer itself was something of a hybrid, since it joined our older analog computer with the new Link Mark 11 digital computer. While the cockpit itself was patterned after that of the cancelled Dinosaur vehicle, the motion system offered a wider range of motion than had ever been provided before. The trainer could tilt through plus and minus 90 degrees, and thus could put the pilot in the correct position for each phase of the mission. We also got into something new and revolutionary in visual presentations on this program, for in order to allow for realism, we developed a computer controlled projection system which was mounted in front of the capsule and provided views of the earth, moon and stars at the appropriate time and attitude of the vehicle. Our team mates in the development and manufacture of this way out visual system were the Farrand Company and the American Machine and Foundry Company (AMF), who built a large portion of the motion system.

As sometimes happens with new projects where there is no way to calculate the costs or gauge the complexity of the device we found that we had underestimated the cost of completing this "one of a kind" simulator. This necessitated a series of anxious meetings with the Air Force systems Command headquarters. At length, after justifying our overruns and verifying that the unit would be completed as now forecast, we satisfied our questioners and were able to finish the job.

With the project completed, a dedication was arranged just prior to Christmas 1964. It turned out to be a great day for us, and a memorable one for General McConnell, then Vice-Chief of the Air Force. He had decided to attend the ceremony, and was seated next to me as the speech making got underway. Soon he was called away to accept a telephone call from Washington. When he returned he announced with some pride that President Johnson had just nominated him to be Chief of Staff of the Air Force.

At the time, we felt that the T-27 probably represented the ultimate in space simulation, and in fact it probably did. We went on however to provide some of the hardware which was subsequently used in the simulation complex being developed by the McDonnell Company for the Gemini Program. We kept our hand in space in a number of other ways until the time came to compete for the design and development of the Apollo and Lunar Excursion Module Simulators. The actual Apollo was being constructed by North American Rockwell Corporation, and the LEM by Grumman. The specifications called for all instrument, communication and visual systems that might be needed for training the astronauts for the moon landing missions. After an initial sifting, five finalists emerged as the major competitors. Curtiss-Wright, Goodyear, Melpar, the Honeywell-ACF electronics team and Link. Each of the contenders had provided masses of information and had made many presentations to the primary contractors and the NASA evaluators. Finally only Link and Melpar remained. Things came to a head, when one day each finalist was to make his complete presentation to the combined North American, Grumman, NASA evaluation team, 150 strong. John Hunt, Bob Campbell, later to become Link's President, Jim McGowan, who later became Senior Vice President, Doc Campbell, our Controller, and I represented Link. We offered reams of technical material and stacks of drawings and detailed diagrams and naturally we emphasized our experience in a variety of space projects. When it was over we waited. And waited. Several weeks went by without a word. Finally one fine day the telephone rang, and the caller announced that we had been selected to negotiate a final agreement. This was a time consuming, though satisfying, experience, and helped get many of our problems out in the open. What many people didn't understand was that there was a vast difference between operational hardware and simulator hardware. While every piece of the real Apollo had to be, and was meticulously constructed, of the best material known to man, comparable pieces of the simulator only had to appear to be. Similarly, minor changes in the actual Apollo could often be easily accomplished. But if the change affected several systems, we might have to work for days to bring the simulator around to the point where it was reflecting what would happen in the real thing.

When the agreement was concluded and signed, we were proud, pleased and at the same time apprehensive. We were about to undertake design and construction of the largest simulator ever built, yet we knew that it would perforce have to be based on data that while probably correct, still represented only the best guesses, conjecture and hunches of the engineering community associated with NASA and its contractors.

As things got underway, it became clear that many of the problems we had anticipated were not going to be, in part because the use of the simulator was in itself changing appreciably. For example, we spent an inordinate amount of time on the waste disposal system in the simulator. We wanted it to duplicate precisely what was in the airborne Apollo since originally it was contemplated that astronauts would actually be spending days at a time in the simulator. As it turned out our fine waste disposal system was largely ignored since the better use of the simulator seemed to be in rehearsing interminably some critical period in the mission when instrument readings and correct human responses were essential to the safety of the mission. I have seen astronauts practice some critical three or four minute phases literally dozens of times.

As it turned out the astronauts trained for several years in the simulators before the time came for first flight. It seems logical to us that the split second timing and perfect machine-human interface that resulted during flight was in large part the work of the constant drill in the simulators.

Today the astronauts can practice an entire mission in their simulators. They start at T minus 60 seconds and perform all the standard immediate pre-launch actions working up to liftoff. Then they are on their way. Next, they run through the activity necessary to achieve earth orbit and soon they are circling the globe. Translunar injection and coast follow. Then the moon appears, at first quite small and later looms larger as the target comes into view. Depending on the mission objectives, lunar descent, landing and ascent can be rehearsed then, before rendezvous and docking are called for. Finally, the return to earth and reentry complete the program. During the entire mission, all radio and visual cues are duplicated and the instruments report the capsule's condition. The only shortcut that is allowed in this simulated moon flight is a speed-up button that moves the flight along at thirty times its normal speed so that astronauts may concentrate on critical phases of the mission without having to go through long periods of inactivity. Of course, there is a freeze button that can stop the action at any point as well as a reset switch that the controller can use to reverse the flight so that a phase of the mission can be rerun.

As we started the development of the Apollo simulator, we realized that unlike any other we had built, our simulator was going to provide virtually all the experience most of the astronauts were going to get before they had to go out and do their real thing. Since the Apollo capsule itself is a one-time machine and since many of the astronauts had not had previous space flights, we were struck by the fact that whatever we could build into the simulator was a main resource for the Apollo crew to learn about its vehicle. True, there were many other special exercises that were designed to familiarize the astronauts with some of the unique aspects of space flight. Weightlessness was achieved by taking the crews aloft in a huge KC-135 cargo plane and flying a parabolic trajectory. In effect, this means the aircraft dives out from under the astronauts so they can float around the padded interior of the plane for about thirty seconds. G forces can be simulated in a giant centrifuge that whirls its victims in a wide circle. But providing the opportunity to live and work in the cramped quarters of Apollo was up to us.

We started by building replicas of the spacecraft itself and then installing the dozens of switches, dials, controls and displays that fill the interior of the capsule. Next came the monumental job of wiring each of these so that it would respond as it should during a flight. To complicate matters further, many of the indicators had to be constructed in a way whereby one or more of them could be singled out to give a positive indication of trouble. Similarly, each also had to automatically respond to corrective action. Following this exercise, we installed all the physical appurtenances of the capsule and, lastly, the working systems were put aboard.

With the capsule precisely duplicated, our work was only half done, for the task of providing the aural cues and visual system remained. Sounds of engine burn and lift-off buffeting were recorded and made ready for triggering at the appropriate time. The visual simulation system for the AMS and LMS used over ten tons of lenses, mirrors and film, a great deal of it designed by the Farrand Company. Separate units have been prepared for each of the four windows in the Apollo and the three portholes of the Lunar module. Thus a spaceman may look out one window of the Apollo simulator and see the earth receding in the distance, while a glance out another window may show the stars and moon growing in size. Of course, the stars must be positioned in the view with such accuracy that celestial fixes can be made by using a sextant.

One of the little niceties that is often observed when a piece of gear as massive and complex as the Apollo simulator is delivered is that the contractor gets to take one of the first rides in the machine. It had consequently been agreed that Joe Shea, NASA Apollo project manager, and I would make one of the first flights in the Apollo Mission Simulator. At the time of delivery to the Houston Space Center we were all staggered by its enormous size even though we had built it. It had formerly occupied most of a hangar at Broome County Airport in Binghamton where we had constructed a huge "clean room" in which the simulator had taken shape. Although it was impressive there, it took on a new dimension when set in its quarters at Houston.

As the team for the first ride readied itself and the simulator was fine tuned for its initial launch, Captain Kellenberg of the USAF, who had been assigned to NASA, was to be in the middle couch while Joe Shea was in the left command couch, and I was in the right. There is no denying that I had looked forward to this flight and I suppose was, in a sense, living one of my daydreams of being an astronaut. As was inevitable, there were a few last minute adjustments to make, and we all had some coffee while things were put right. We had a short briefing then, and enjoyed some more coffee before climbing aboard. We got launched smoothly and then suffered a glitch that took an hour or so to fix, and then continued our mission. After several hours it became apparent to me that unless I was to initiate our waste disposal system I was going to have to bail out onto the simulated ground. When on our descent from orbit another small malfunction occurred, I decided to call a Mayday, and although we were at a simulated 400,000 feet happily we were actually a mere 13 feet above the floor.

With the Apollo Mission Simulator (AMS) delivered we next turned our attention to making certain the Lunar Module Mission Simulator would come along on time, and would blend successfully with the AMS. Ray Long, who later was to be President of Link, was our project manager and had been working with Grumman on the LEM. Grumman had provided excellent math models for the computers of the LEM and this contributed to the simulator progressing much more smoothly and rapidly than had been true of Apollo. Credit too for this feat must go in part to Dick

Taylor who was able to work out a special test philosophy that allowed us to work out testing on an integrated basis rather than step by step. Though there was some risk in testing this way instead of piece by piece, our gamble seemed to be justified when after delivery (15 days ahead of schedule) the quality control people could find only six minor discrepancies.

Our contract called for the delivery of three Apollo mission simulators and two LEMs, but with these in NASA's hands, our work was far from finished. Our agreement specified that we would maintain and modify these as necessary and the varying objectives of each mission kept us making changes in each constantly. At first there was something of a problem in deciding how to keep each simulator working to best advantage when astronaut teams were training for flights with differing objectives and taking place at different times. Finally it was decided that the simulator at Cape Kennedy would be patterned for the next mission to fly and the others at Houston would be kept in readiness for future missions. This worked quite satisfactorily but increased the number of our staff people to a point where at the peak of activity we had as many as 650 people working at Cape Kennedy and Houston.

Though the NASA team itself was one of the most hard working and dedicated groups of people I or the Link staff had ever worked with, there were lighter moments in the long hours of concentrated effort. As word of the wonders of the Apollo simulators spread around the country and indeed around the world, the visits of the celebrated often provided the occasion for a break in the routine. It also offered an opportunity for the playing of an in-house joke on some of the visitors. Of course most of the people who came to view the simulator wanted to take a simulated flight to the moon and in most cases they were given one. Quite by accident our test teams had discovered that as the television camera of the visual system approached the model of the moon the presence of an earthbound fly on the "moon surface" gave the appearance of an enormous monster standing grotesquely among the craters. Needless to say, this surprise was repeated for a few visitors taking their first moon flight and the result was so gratifying that variations and refinements were soon made a part of any celebrity's trip. Thus when now President of France, Pompidou, came swooping down to the moon's face, what should he see peeping out from behind a moon rock but a small replica of the Eiffel Tower. And when Arnold Palmer, himself a pilot of his own airplane, prepared for landing on the moon, the spot that had been chosen for his contact turned out to be a tiny putting green with a flag stuck in the hole. It must be admitted too that a variety of bugs and beetles were occasionally sacrificed to provide a notable visitor with the shock of seeing what appeared to be a monster on the moon.

One of the most difficult problems we continued to face during the shakedown period of preparation for the first Apollo flight was the magnitude of the task of modifying the simulator to reflect modification in the Apollo vehicle. An example of this may be seen when well into the training period for the first flight great concern developed over what would happen if one of the guidance boosters malfunctioned. At that time little could be done to remedy such a problem and, accordingly, it was decided to install a backup guidance system which would allow the astronauts to fly manually during the translunar insertion phase. Once the decision was made the Apollo vehicle was modified by a moderate amount of new hardware and the addition of a single toggle switch in the cockpit. These changes were noted by the addition of a small digital program to the software of the guidance computer.

For us, however, it was a different story. After weeks of study we found it necessary to add an entirely new digital computer to the bank plus a 25,000 word program.

On many occasions prior to the fateful Apollo 13 flight, Ray Long, President of Link Division of Singer-General Precision, and Ken Butler, Engineering, had considered the possibility of the Apollo simulators acting as an immediate test bed to develop emergency procedures in the event of a malfunction during an actual Apollo mission. Thus, when Astronaut Lovell's "Hey, we've got a problem," came crackling across the expanse of space, they and many of the Link and NASA experts were ready to see what role the simulators could play in helping to solve the problem.

That role quickly became clear when, immediately following the announcement of the explosion aboard "XIII," Astronaut Eugene A. Cernan headed for the simulator room late on that Monday night and called out, "Keep 'em running." And keep 'em running they did for that entire momentous week. It was a week during which we and everyone in our company were proud of the simulators built and maintained by the Link Division for NASA. The role the simulators played in helping to bring back safely the moon-bound astronauts was summarized in *The New York Times* this way: "The countless improvisations that nursed the crippled spacecraft along were in large measure the product of an extraordinarily elaborate assembly of simulators at the Manned Spacecraft Center in Houston and elsewhere. Every makeshift procedure carried out in space was first tried out on earth and rejected if the simulators showed it to be dangerous or impractical."

And following the successful return to earth a national radio commentator reported, "The maneuvers performed this morning were done as they had been worked out by simulation."

During the week more than a dozen astronauts "flew" the simulators, meticulously testing the unorthodox procedures that saved their colleagues' lives. At one point, five men— including the chief of the astronauts, Donald K. Slayton— were jammed into the LM simulator, which is designed to hold only two.

Among the astronauts who participated in the testing was Thomas K. Mattingly, II, who had been scrubbed from the Apollo 13 flight because of exposure to measles. Mattingly, who seemed blotch-free, spent an entire night trying out re-entry plans, recommending a number of procedural changes which were adopted.

After the pinpoint splashdown, Jerry Purser, who directs Link's operations at both the Cape and Houston, sat in his office, in which is displayed a NASA citation for Link's "outstanding contributions" to the Apollo program.

Reflecting on the eventful week, he said: "Even more significant than the emergency problems which were solved on the simulators was the training which they had provided the Apollo 13 crew. This training greatly increased their chances of survival."

The analysis of malfunctions that may result in emergencies in the real vehicle is a highly skilled task that requires a complete understanding of the way the computers have been programmed. In a way it demands that one think as the computer acts. At the same time, solutions to problems that might occur need the total comprehension of the elements of the mathematical formulae that represent the performance of the flight. The same principles obtain when malfunctions occur in the simulator itself. There have been many occasions when men have worked for 30 or 40 hours straight to track down the cause of a problem that interrupted training.

The most frustrating kind of mechanical fault that occasionally plagues both the Apollo itself as well as the simulators is known as the intermittent. It often is the result of a loose connection or some other relatively small error in bringing together the miles of wires and hundreds of fittings that are the heart of Apollo and of its simulator. The maddening characteristic of the intermittent is that it will appear as mysteriously as it, for no apparent reason, will disappear. Often the fix will require going back to the original design programs and painstakingly reviewing and inspecting every possible area of trouble. And, of course, once an intermittent develops, no one can really rest until it is tracked down and fixed. While I could not name all those whose determination and dedication contributed to the success of our part of the Apollo program, one name does stick with me. True, it is an unusual name, but I also recall his working methodically for one full 24 hour stretch tracking down a glitch. His name is Shafik Tabeek and he was typical of many others.

Needless to say, there were occasions when some innocent bystander inadvertently brought things to a standstill. On one such occasion with a launch just a month away and the entire AMS and LEM simulators tied together and the primary crew training intensively, a guard walked into the room, checked some fire extinguishers and putting his portable radio transmitter to his lips reported to his headquarters that all was well. At that instant the entire array of computers dropped out and everything came to a standstill. Nobody had noticed the guard transmitting, and as he stood aside watching the bedlam that was going on, people tried to find out what had happened. No one suspected that his walkie-talkie was the cause of the blackout. After a half-hour of searching the guard transmitted again to report he was moving on to another building when someone wondered if his stray radio signal could have caused the trouble. Sure enough it developed that the transmission had so unnerved the sensitive computers that they temporarily went beserk. The diligent guards were asked to do their inspecting during off-hours after that.

The question of how committed to manned space exploration the United States will continue to be remains open. There are many people who believe that unmanned vehicles can now perform almost as well and accomplish as much as is possible with manned flights. I believe that while there is room for both forms of exploration men still offer the most efficient and effective means of probing the mysteries of space.

NASA, too, seems to feel that given the support it needs, astronaut flights offer the best opportunity for making further advances in space. One of its next ventures includes lofting into orbit a Saturn 4B vehicle refitted to serve as a laboratory in space. Here in "SkyLab" astronauts will live for as long as a month studying the heavens and experiencing the problems of prolonged space living. To our great satisfaction we have been chosen to build the SkyLab simulator. Thus the team that worked so well together on Apollo and Lem can be kept together for work on another great manned space mission.

While much of our most recent experience has been with manned vehicles we have taken part in some of the work with remotely controlled vehicles. At the time of the un-manned Ranger moon shots we worked with the Jet Propulsion Laboratory and built a space-ground handling system. The purpose of this effort was to devise ways of receiving and making usable, data sent from an unmanned probe. Basically what we tried to do was to translate and purify the torrent of information that poured from the vehicle as it journeyed in space. With our system set up at the Jet Propulsion Laboratory the great moment was in receiving the telemetric data coming back from Ranger 9. This data was collected, organized and placed in a form that could be transmitted over commercial television. We in our homes were able to see pictures from Ranger 9 in real time as it plunged onto the Moon's surface. More recently, on a Mariner shot the data was returned with the pictures and observations taken. The data left a question concerning the nature and content of the ice cap at the pole. With our equipment, the data was normalized and all extraneous noise removed from the pictures so scientists were able to make much more meaningful use of it.

Many of us have believed that simulation in training represents one of the most effective and efficient forms of teaching techniques. As with many theses proof comes only in a pure environment. Too many pilots had already learned to fly when the trainer was invented for us to be able to prove its total value. Space flight, however, was completely new so that we had perfect conditions under which to apply simulation and thus prove its full potential. The astronauts supported this full application completely. The results were proof that indeed simulation saves lives and helps to develop proficiency, even when the real machine is not yet available for use.

9

The Future Unlimited

Our crystal ball may be cloudy, but it is hard to see how the future for the use of simulators can be anything but bright. There is an increasing appreciation on the part of many industries of the benefits of teaching necessary skills by use of simulators rather than by osmosis. As an example, the railroad and shipping businesses are gradually recognizing that simulators can help train locomotive engineers and ship captains faster and more effectively than was ever done in the traditional apprentice method.

In the development of these and other educational and instructional devices we are fortunate to have the enthusiastic support of our corporate group. When General Precision joined with The Singer Company in 1968 there was some apprehension in the Link group about the continuing interest of the new corporation in the field of simulation. As it has turned out, the opportunity to join with The Singer Company and the evolution of Link's technological skills have brought about many developments which further broaden the horizon for simulation and for Link. Only by this could we have made the great strides that we have achieved.

Organizationally, Singer has decided that it should orient its activities in areas which help solve certain important needs of mankind. Also, Singer management believes that to be truly successful and of greatest service, the interests of a corporation should be international. Donald P. Kircher, Singer Chairman and President, early after our joining Singer, created an Education and Training Group as one of the six major groups of Singer activity. This included the Link, Graflex, and Society for Visual Education companies, and the operation of a Job Corps camp at Camp Breckinridge in Morganfield, Kentucky, the General Precision Laboratories' television products and other similarly associated training products. This had an added effect of making Link the prime thrust of one of the country's major corporation's effort in the field of Education and Training. At the same time, the group was encouraged to look at world-wide needs, and so today Singer-Link finds itself working closely with the Link-Miles organization in Lancing, England, which produces simulation and training devices for a wide variety of vehicles, and the Mitsubishi Precision Company in Japan, which produces a similar series of products for the Far Eastern market.

The Singer Company's appreciation of the benefits of an alliance with General Precision were perhaps best summed up in the President's letter to the stockholders in the Annual Report. Mr. Kircher said in part:

The year 1968 was a particularly eventful one for The Singer Company. It marked the completion of another major advance in our evolution from an enterprise engaged primarily in the production and sale of a single product to one with major operations in five broad business areas and with important commitments and capabilities in advanced technology. The merger last July with

General Precision Equipment Corporation, and the subsequent realignment of operating units within the combined enterprise into groups serving specific major markets, has brought new strength and opportunity to the entire Singer organization.

These were times of analyses and redirection for Singer to make the most of the joining of the two companies. The President acknowledged this in another part of the Annual Report message.

We have endeavored to discipline our diversification activities, whether by merger, acquisition or by internal development, so as to produce and maintain a well-balanced cohesive enterprise, the segments of which would be operationally related and mutually reinforcing. The GPE merger is further manifestation of this philosophy. In setting the course of our diversification program at its inception we recognized that one of its goals should be an increasing involvement in advanced technical activities. This was achieved step-by-step with the acquisition of HRB, the later acquisition of several small instrument companies, the acquisition of Friden, and finally the GPE merger, with the whole process being accompanied and encouraged by increasingly large internal investment in engineering, product development and research, both in the older segments of the Company and those more recently acquired. Today we are a major technology company with annual sales of more than a half billion dollars in areas which are technically advanced. As another indicator of our technical position, we are today considered the fifteenth largest electronic company in American industry with sales of electronic products and services which exceed the volume of the entire company at the time the present management became responsible for the Company's direction.

A recent example of the broader acceptance of simulators by industries outside the aviation space or automotive field was evidenced recently when, after some years of study and analysis of their particular problems, we received an order for a locomotive and train simulator from the Santa Fe Railroad. Designed to train prospective locomotive engine men and to upgrade the skills of present engineers, the SD-45 locomotive simulator was made to order for Santa Fe, but is adaptable to any railroad. In placing the order, John S. Reed, President of Santa Fe, said, "This purchase culminates over two years of research which included a study of simulator training devices used by the armed forces and commercial airlines, as well as inspection of prototype railway training devices used in England. After reviewing the traditional railway learning process of education by osmosis wherein an employee learns primarily from association with experienced personnel and comparing that with the results that could be obtained by using a simulator, our conclusion is that the cost of a simulator is justified."

The SD-45 locomotive simulator we produced for Santa Fe is in many ways comparable to the most advanced simulators produced for the airlines. It has motion, visual and sound systems, and uses state-of-the-art digital computers. Physically the simulator duplicates the operator's side of an SD-45 diesel locomotive cab. All of the gages, controls and levers are in place as they would be in the real thing. At the rear of the cab is the instructor's station, whose console is equipped with all the capability of introducing problems and malfunctions with which the trainee has to cope. The simulator was designed to give the prospective engineman the feel of a wide variety of train configurations of different tonnages. He is expected to be able to gage his time in getting up to speed and the distance required to stop a heavily loaded freight train.

One of the unusual requirements of the SD-45 was that it be able to fit inside a railroad car so that it could be moved from place to place throughout the Santa Fe system. In this way, trainmen didn't have to come to a central location for their instruction, but instead the simulator could be brought to the student.

Convenient as this was for the trainee, the installation caused us no end of problems, for we had to stabilize the railroad car itself before we could build the motion system for the simulator. We devised a means of jacking up the car itself and tying it to the rails so that as the heavy simulator inside the car heaved and shuddered to duplicate the motion of a railroad cab, the car would remain stationary. We then installed the hydraulic motion system in the floor of the car and rigged it to simulate fore and aft shock at the times when a link-up with cars was called for. Additionally, we built in a side sway and roll as well as vibrations in the floor of the cab to give the feel of travelling over rails at high speed.

The visual system was as complex as those in some of the most advanced aircraft simulators. As the engineman looked through his viewing window, he saw scenes that accurately reflected what we would encounter on a run. The rear projection screen showed up to 4000 feet of 16 mm movies depicting both routine and emergency situations, including signal compliance, meeting and passing point situations and innumerable other incidents requiring the engineer to take specific action. A unique lens mounted before the front window provided images up to infinity with realistic depth of field. This lens forced the viewer to refocus his eyes as he would in the real world when looking at varying distances. A track and ballast simulator resembling a treadmill was located below the cab's right window. Movement of the belt is synchronized with the locomotive's speed up to ten miles an hour, an important visual cue for an engineman when starting a train.

Complementing the visual realism were all important sounds, which are electronically generated and stereophonic. An air compressor duplicates the air sounds within the cab. The system employs Link's standard line of solid-state sound-generation printed circuit cards under control of the digital computer.

All subsystems are synchronized and operated by a high-speed digital computer that solves in real time the math model equations governing locomotive characteristics, track conditions, train loads and track profile.

Another unusual simulator order was recently placed by Babcock and Wilcox Company requiring us to construct a Nuclear Power Plant Training Simulator. The simulator complex consists of the nuclear power plant control consoles, with the instructor's console and computer complex located in a separate room overlooking the power plant control consoles. The operator's control consoles are an exact duplicate of B&W's pressurized water reactor console. Over 2000 analog and digital switches and indicators are dynamically driven and sensed by a Link GP-4B computer, the "heart" of the simulator.

The Link reactor simulator is used to train operators in startup, maneuvering under normal and emergency conditions, and shutdowns of an actual atomic reactor power plant. The instructor is able to introduce 100 malfunctions to the student operator in complete safety. Preselected casualty drills and summaries of student performance are produced automatically by the GP-4B computer. The simulator provides an economical and efficient means of training operators in all aspects of the operation of a nuclear reactor power plant. The associated training programs prepare the trainee for the Atomic Energy Commission Reactor Operator licensing examination.

We subsequently received a second order for a Nuclear Reactor Trainer from Combustion Engineering Co. of Hartford, Connecticut.

As in other cases, the reactor simulator serves both the purpose of economy and of safety. There is a potential for decrease in nuclear safety posture through human error. Training minimizes this risk. Regulations require a nuclear power plant operator to have classroom instruction, to observe actual operation for six months, and to participate in two power plant startups. These same regulations allow substitution of simulator time for some of the observation and startup requirements. Inasmuch as a single shutdown and startup can cost in excess of $100,000, the saving from simulator use in training is significant.

It seems that as any vehicle and the environment in which it operates grows more complex, a simulator is an inevitability. Recently the Masters Mates and Pilots Union came to us and asked us to build a ship's bridge simulator so that the union members can be trained for advancement. It has, of course, been long recognized that formal scholastic training in navigation and ship handling is a prerequisite for command. When it comes to "conning" a ship, however, it has always been generally accepted that experience is the best teacher. But in many instances, experience in emergency situations is hard to come by and proficiency in the latest handling techniques, under both normal and emergency conditions, is all but impossible to achieve. An example of the shortcomings of the traditional way of doing things was mentioned in the Bowditch *American Practical Navigator,* published by the U.S. Hydrographic Office:

> Radar has not materially reduced the number of collisions, as might have been anticipated. This may be due to any number of reasons, or probably to a combination of several. Among these are the following: uncertainty as to whether the other vessel has radar, failure to use radar information, lack of confidence in radar, lack of appreciation of the limitations of radar, failure to act promptly, failure to establish prompt communication with the other vessel, uncertainty as to obligation under rules of the road, misinterpretation of radar information, difficulty of adequately visualizing a situation presented on a radar scope and lack of knowledge of use to be made of radar information. Most of these can be summed up as lack of adequate training. There is record of radar actually having been removed from vessels because it was considered a collision hazard. A better remedy would undoubtedly have been to instruct ships' personnel in proper use of this valuable aid.

To help meet these needs we designed the first marine collision avoidance trainer. This radar simulator, called CART (Collision Avoidance Radar Trainer) has bridged this training gap and allows ships' officers to be projected repeatedly and safely into realistic shipboard situations. Incidentally,

CART is the first known device which utilizes information stored in a digital computer memory to generate real-time land-mass video signals for presentation on a radar console. With these digital processing techniques, situations are presented on the trainer radar scope which prove to be equally realistic to the inexperienced officer operating a simulated ship on the open consoles. Basic trainees can be stationed at repeaters to observe the maneuvers of the two own-ships and four targets through the simulated channel. Thus they become familiar with the exercise parameters and numerous problems that may be encountered during the exercise.

"The obvious beauty of such training," say school officials, "is the capability of presenting controlled realistic practical ship-handling exercises to a large group of students without the expense of vessel operation or the danger of collision. The student and his vessel can be placed in danger of collision or grounding in order to test reactions. He can also practice piloting his vessel with radar just as would be done in a pea-soup fog. The only limitations as to what can be done . . . are human—the imagination of the instructor and the ability of the programmer."

The Link CART uses the inherent flexibility and accuracy of digital computation to generate real-time radar signals for presentation on a radar console. Since it utilizes a stored computer program, video characteristics are changed in a few minutes by feeding information on a punched tape computer memory via a high-speed tape reader. The simulator presents a moving radar picture to the student just as if he were on board ship. He can control the direction and speed of his vessel while observing the exact coastline and navigational aids of a specific area, as well as five other moving vessels, four whose direction and speed are controlled by the instructor and one that is controlled by the student. The students use their radar sets and controls exactly as they would at sea. The instructor can read the distance and direction between vessels instantaneously as the exercise progresses.

Each trainee station contains a Main Propulsion Control (RPM), Helm Control (rudder) and a Compass Repeater and Speed (log) Readout. The simulation of own-ship dynamic response is a function of time-controlled rates which can be modified by the instructor to approximate a wide range of vessel tonnage and propulsion capacities. This simulation, in turn, determines normal time delay and response rate characteristics of the simulated own-ship. The instructor has controls for maneuvering four target ships and for inserting six fixed targets anywhere within the gaming area. Thus, traffic in the area, as well as the other own-ship position, is dynamically displayed to the trainee as the problem progresses. As own-ship position changes within the simulated area, aspect angle, radar shadow masking and line-of-sight limitations control the video presented on the radar displays. Abnormal weather, sea clutter, own-ship superstructure masking and noise can be inserted by the instructor.

Action required by the student to control the simulated own-ship course and speed in order to navigate buoyed navigational channels and avoid ship traffic in the harbor area becomes immediately apparent. A unique feature of such a training system is the capability of presenting controlled and realistic ship handling exercises to a large group of students without the expense of actual vessel operation.

A significant training feature incorporated in CART allows the student to maneuver in a simulated seaward shipping lane (out of contact with land-mass radar returns). Since a junior officer will most likely be confronted with the responsibility for proper radar operation and interpretation during a real-world situation of this nature, the training value of this feature cannot be overemphasized. Re-creation (performed at the U. S. Army Transportation School) of both the Andria-Doria and Stockholm radar displays on a second-by-second basis as they appeared before their collision, provides an unusual and graphic illustration of the versatility of CART when used for collision evaluation and reconstruction studies. Any one who witnesses such a re-creation would surely recognize a similar real-life situation developing long before another such collision became imminent.

Our newest watercraft simulator, named the collision avoidance and underway watch trainer, was designed to meet the growing need for precise handling of the giant oil tankers now being built in such profusion. While this new simulator has many similarities to CART, it incorporates many improvements. The major elements are a reproduction of the bridge of one of the new jumbo tankers and the adjoining chart room. The students operate the bridge controls as they would on the ship, and signals flow to a computer which moves the ship along the planned route. Once again the computer contains all the information necessary to make the voyage conform to what would actually be experienced. Buoys, lights, channels and hazards to navigation are all there, and the trainee must steer his ship with the skill and accuracy required of a master.

Visual presentations as seen from the bridge can be varied to simulate the lights of a harbor or the darkness of the open sea and a variety of weather conditions can be presented including rain, fog and haze. The instructor in this massive simulator can present problems that require quick action and call for thorough knowledge of how slowly the giant craft responds. In one such test the instructor can introduce the lights of an approaching ship looming through the fog. As the lights come closer, the student captain must determine the correct moves to make even if the other ship fails to heed the proper passing procedure.

Captain O'Callahan, head of the Masters, Mates and Pilots union, has also enlarged the new training center in Maryland to include a huge cargo loading simulator with pumping control stations similar to what is used to fill up the new breed of jumbo tanker.

There seems to be little doubt that the enormous cost in lives and property of private boating accidents will some day encourage the development of simulators to train weekend sailors in the rudiments of boating. But the area of training and testing that seems to offer the greatest opportunity for progress is automobile simulators.

Most traffic safety experts and knowledgeable educators believe quality driver education programs in high school offer the greatest hope for the future. At the present, less than half the school population has an opportunity to learn to drive in school. The major reason is the great cost of providing cars and instructors. The automobile industry helped by donating some training cars, and the insurance industry reduced rates for graduates of driver education programs, but it was not enough. A new approach was needed. A new method had to be devised that would provide major economies and, at the same time, improve the quality of the traditional driver education course.

To us the heart of the answer was driver training simulators. We took the basic solid state digital technology that was used in the large airline and space simulators and built an automobile driver trainer that could train a student and simultaneously measure his performance by comparing the result against a predetermined standard. When he is not doing what is called for in use of brakes and lights and speed and steering, we can alert him to the error and indicate corrective action.

Our new driving simulator, introduced to the educational community in 1965, contains several unique features that are firsts in the industry. These include an individual instructor-student communication system for each trainee, and a visual display on the instructor's console that enables him to monitor each driver's performance. And, the length of the new "car" is shorter than our older simulators, so that one-third more units may be installed in the same amount of classroom space. The instructor can check students' braking, steering and signaling, as well as his speed and general control of the car.

The new Link Driving Simulator resembles the driver's side of a late model car and includes a completely functional panel. The simulator can be "driven" either with automatic or manual shift and incorporates many of the required safety features on new cars, including a retractable seat belt and shoulder harness, an emergency flasher, a parking brake and a seatbelt warning light as standard equipment. Through the use of full-color Cinemascope films provided by the Allstate Insurance Company, the student can practice driving under a wide variety of conditions—during day and night, on dry and wet roads, and on highways and congested city streets.

Our newest entry in the field of automotive simulators is one in which we hope to aid in a major research program being undertaken by the Federal Highway Administration. Unfortunately, much of the information on highway accidents is collected after the fact and tragically in many instances, many of the victims are not able to report what happened. In an effort to find answers to the question of what happened, we are developing a device that will allow hundreds of subjects to be tested in accident situations to find as nearly as possible what can be done to improve the automotive accident record.

Named the Vehicle Research Simulator, the basic trainer is a reproduction of the driver's side of a late-model car. It includes all of the necessary indicators and equipment that most cars afford today. Behind this "car," however, is a vastly complex array of testing equipment that can put our driver through some of the most demanding experiences of his driving career. A visual system presents a wide variety of road surfaces and conditions and introduces a mixture of light and heavy traffic. Traffic signs are presented in a variety of colors and sizes and the sounds of the road and of traffic are accurately introduced. In this realistic environment, our driver can be tested and examined under near actual conditions. His reflexes and responses to road hazards can be measured and his reaction to other driver faults gaged. Each of the subjects tested in this program is being examined, too, for mental stress prior to his test since it has long been suspected that a driver's mental state often determines how safely he drives.

By giving the same quota of problems to hundreds of different drivers, gaging the response and measuring the result, it is hoped that many accidents that go unexplained can be understood and the cause corrected.

The technological evolution has taken the form of extension of the technology required for simulation to allied product areas. For example, one of the problems which education and the nation generally face is that of the storage and retrieval of information. In the mid-1950s, Link developed a particular skill in the use of flying spot scanner techniques for the simulation of radar signals that one might see while flying over land and sea. We call this "Land Mass Simulation." It is possible by the closed loop operation of a flying spot scanner system, to produce, through the use of photographic transparencies, a simulation of the picture that one would see on a radar scope in an airplane when flying over some given segment of the earth. This skill in using a flying spot scanner to read a transparency was then extrapolated into the skill to write pictures on film from digital signals sent back from space. A device to do this was called the Spacecraft Television Ground Data Handling System, which Link built under contract to Jet Propulsion Laboratories (JPL).

This ground data handling system has been instrumental in many of our space shots, including Ranger and Surveyor. Also, one of its most recent triumphs was its use to record information from the Mariner shot. You may recall that there was a great deal of debate as to the nature of the material found around the polar caps of Mars. Photographs that had been corrected were used in trying to determine what the precise nature of the ice was. The Spacecraft Television Ground Data Handling System is able to take data recorded from space and to purify the information so that extraneous signals and information are removed. The result is that the pictures more accurately reflect what the camera has seen in space and scientists are able to determine more precisely what it is they are seeing.

Perhaps you remember seeing on television a picture of the Ranger Nine as it plunged into the moon. The data coming back from the Ranger was recorded and made suitable for real-time commercial television operation by the Link unit in conjunction with JPL engineers working with NASA. Link also obtained a number of other contracts in the field of flying spot scanner technology, including one for the Army, which was a project designed to allow one to take a microfilm of a drawing, for example, and allow the operator to update the drawing by changing call-outs, dimensions, part numbers, etc., through a computer without having to redraw the drawing.

Subsequent to this, the Transamerica Corporation came to Link wondering if it would be interested in attempting to build a complete data storage and retrieval system which would contain title insurance data on a magnetic tape to allow easy recovery. Link designed such a system for them. It was felt to be so good that Transamerica became interested in attempting to market this data and storage retrieval unit to other companies who might have a similar use, such as a credit card company or perhaps a police department or a law enforcement agency. The net result of this has been the formulation of a joint venture by Transamerica and The Singer

Company to design and market data storage and retrieval systems containing large amounts of data which need to be stored, and where rapid access and retrieval with the ability to change the data is required. Its initial use will be in libraries for business. Conceivably, it may well one day fit libraries for schools.

Also, as an outgrowth of the experience in working with microfilm, Link has developed a micrographic system for the automatic reading and storing of microfilm information in digital form on a computer. The ability to compress this information and to operate on it in the sense of changing its order prior to reprinting on microfilm makes it a highly useful tool for business, since it is able to include such information as engineering data where large amounts of alphanumeric and graphical data must be recorded and monitored. A unique feature of the Link machine is its speed and accuracy which enables it to plot high quality graphic information. For example, if a set of equations for a propeller blade were entered into a computer and one wished to plot some characteristic in relation to propeller blade angle, it would be possible for the computer to compute the values for different blade angles and to draw that information directly on microfilm in graphic form, as contrasted with the more traditional means of printing out a series of numbers, which would then be plotted by hand before one could see the graphic representation of the data of interest. These particular applications are an outgrowth of the basic technology which first took form as a radar land mass simulator designed for training. It may well be that the same technical skill has now been able to assist in producing tools for educators to be used in training in many different fields.

Another example of the extension of Link technology in the general field of education, a result of our merger with Singer, is their development of a multi-media device which has the ability to program the operation of nine separate events; for example, turning off room lights, turning on projector "A," turning on projector "B," turning that off and turning on slide projector "C," and then turning back on the room lights, etc. It also has a feature that enables a professor to interrogate up to 240 students in, for example, a lecture hall, who would be called upon to answer some question with one of five alternate choices. The answers are collected by student, with the number of rights and wrongs recorded. Also, the professor is able to tell how many students might have missed any particular question. This is quite useful to him as an instantaneous bit of knowledge in order to gage whether or not his audience is understanding the point he is making. This grows extremely important in large lecture halls such as are characteristic of modern colleges. For example, such a system is in use in the Department of Public Safety in the State of Texas, Berea College in Kentucky, and three high schools in Pennsylvania.

In perspective, it is indeed a long way from the airport in Cortland to the major educational activity of a corporation the size of Singer. This growth is a testimonial to the validity of the training concepts started by Ed Link, and developed, amplified and augmented by those who have followed him.

As I look back on what has been accomplished in the field of simulation, and in spite of myself, marvel at the realistic effects we have been able to achieve, I like to speculate on what the future holds. Initially, I can see in the not too distant future a time when in the automobile field much of the original testing for driver's licenses, as well as the periodic renewal evaluation, will be accomplished by the use of simulators. I am confident that well-designed simulators can provide a more stringent and standardized original test than is given by individual inspectors. And it is certain that more and more states will see the desirability of requiring periodic retesting of drivers. It seems likely that a simulator could be devised that would permit a driver to go to a testing location and place his present license in a machine that would automatically review his past record of summonses, convictions and accidents, if any. On the basis of this information, the applicant would be required to take a simulator driving test, answer some appropriate questions, and if his performance was shown to be inadequate, he would have to take further refresher training before his new license would be issued. If the applicant passed his test, his new license would simply pop out of the machine ready for use.

Though it may be anathema to many pilots, it seems to me that something similar is inevitable in the long-term future for general aviation pilots. The need for periodic reexamination of general aviation pilots has been apparent for many years, but one of the major problems to be faced is the question of finding enough flight instructors to reexamine the thousands of pilots who would come up for renewal of their licenses. Simulators, I believe, could do a major part of this job and at the very least could detect the pilots who should have more training before being allowed to fly.

As the role of the simulator becomes more important in training and testing, I begin to wonder how far we can go in removing individuals from the hazards of learning how to deal with complicated equipment and in avoiding the tragedy that often follows unskilled use of modern machinery. I suspect that literally thousands of opportunities exist for industry to benefit from the proper use of simulators, yet there is the ever present deterrent of economics. We have found that it is virtually impossible to sell a simulator unless there is strong economic justification. The airlines found quite early in the game that although they could train pilots as thoroughly in simulators as they could in an aircraft, they could also save money. They determined that it was impractical to take an airplane out of revenue producing service for weeks at a time to have pilots fly around in it if a simulator could do the job as well. As it has turned out, the evidence is that the simulator can do the job more effectively and for far less money. The same will doubtless prove to be true in many other areas.

As I say, how far can we go in devising ways of removing human beings from the hazards of dealing with complicated and sophisticated machinery and equipment without knowing the shortcomings beforehand? Can we come to a point in time where war could be fought in simulators? It's a mind-boggling thought, but perhaps we are closer to having such a solution to confrontation forced on us than we realize. The costs alone of the present stalemate are staggering, and the anticipated cost of maintaining little more than a standoff runs to trillions of dollars. Two opposing sides now face each other knowing that to precipitate a war could mean the end of our civilization. The question is how long can two sides face each other like the shoot-out in the Western movies without having one or the other draw?

Could there be a simulator alternative? Perhaps. Philosophers, sociologists, students of the human condition and prophets of doom often imply that man's aggressive behavior will not be denied, and war is therefore inevitable. Perhaps then the most we can hope for is that it be bloodless. Can you imagine a situation where two opposing views agree that their differences are irreconcilable and decide "war" is the only answer. The winner is to get major economic benefits and concessions to satisfy his requirements. The loser must pay the price of losing. Both sides establish a value to the real and theoretical weapons in its arsenal, with each value verified by computer. Each side then builds its simulator to include its available forces and to accept and record the counter forces of the opponent. The war is fought and the outcome determined. Fantasy? Improbable? Yes. Impossible? No. Science fiction? Maybe.

We would much rather work with peaceful applications of simulation, but I think we are ready for anything.

INDEX

Academy of Aeronautics, 40
A-C computer system, 112, 127
A-5A trainer, 112–113
Air mail, 51
Airlines, trainers for, 123–133, 136
Aldrin, Edwin "Buzz," 1
Analog computers, 78, 83–84, 106–107, 112, 140
"Angelic" switch, 81
ANT-18 Trainer, 60–62
Apollo Mission Simulator (AMS), 156–158
Apollo 13 flight
recovery of, 12–15
role of simulators in, 164–165
"Aqua Trainer," 57
Armstrong, Neil, 1
Army Air Corps, 52–53
AT-6-SNJ airplane, 60–61
Automotive simulators, 182–184
Aviation, as part of school program, 8

Barnstorming, 34–35
description of, 27–28
reputation of, 22–23, 35
Bennett, Richard "Dick," 23
Bevans, George, 48
B-47 Trainer, 108–109
B-58 bomber aircraft simulator, 113, 145
Blind flying. See Instrument flying

"Blue Box," 4, 69, 120. See also Link Trainer
Blue Heron, 88–89
Bonnalie, Allan, 130–131
Botsford, Dick, 35–36
Bowen, Harold, 27, 45
Bryan Instrument Training School, 61–64

Carmody, Edmund, 73, 74
Carroll, William J., 43–45
CART (Collision Avoidance Radar Trainer), 177–180
C-8 (Model "F"), 119, 125
C-11 Jet Trainer, 79–85, 100, 119
Cernan, Eugene A., 164
Cessna Aircraft Company, 26
Chamberlain, Herb, 74
Chaplin, Sidney, 19–20
CNT (Celestial Navigation Trainer), 65–68, 109–110
Collision avoidance and underway watch trainer, 180–181
Columbus' landing in the new world, Ed Link's interest in, 89–90
Combustion Engineering Co., 176
Computers
choice of, 139–141
design and development of, 105–108

191